AN INTRODUCTION TO
HEAT TRANSFER

AN INTRODUCTION TO
HEAT TRANSFER

BY

M. FISHENDEN
READER IN APPLIED HEAT
IN THE UNIVERSITY OF LONDON
AT IMPERIAL COLLEGE

AND

O. A. SAUNDERS
PROFESSOR OF MECHANICAL ENGINEERING
IN THE UNIVERSITY OF LONDON
AT IMPERIAL COLLEGE

OXFORD
AT THE CLARENDON PRESS

Oxford University Press, Amen House, London E.C. 4

GLASGOW NEW YORK TORONTO MELBOURNE WELLINGTON
BOMBAY CALCUTTA MADRAS CAPE TOWN

Geoffrey Cumberlege, Publisher to the University

First published February 1950
Reprinted with corrections July 1950

PRINTED IN GREAT BRITAIN

PREFACE

In teaching heat transfer the authors have felt the need for a short, concise book suitable for the requirements of university students reading for degrees in various branches of engineering. Indeed, in the present state of knowledge there are many others to whom the more elaborate theoretical treatments of heat transfer are not essential. It is, therefore, hoped that this little book may be of some general interest, especially in industry.

Thanks are due to Mr. J. E. Bacon, B.Sc. (Eng.), A.M.I.Mech.E., for general help in preparing the material, and to the British Iron and Steel Research Association for financial assistance. Mention should also be made of the late Professor C. H. Lander, whose steady interest did so much to further the study of heat transfer in this country.

Our thanks are also due to Professor H. C. Hottel of the Massachusetts Institute of Technology for supplying the drawings from which Figs. 3, 4, 5, and 8 were made. In addition we make grateful acknowledgement to the following: A. Schack and *Stahl und Eisen* for Figs. 11, 12, 13, 14, 15, D. M. Smith and *Engineering* for Fig. 41, and C. F. Bonilla and the American Institute of Chemical Engineers for Figs. 48 and 49 reproduced from *Trans. Am. Inst. Chem. Eng.* 1945, **41**, 755.

M. F.

O. A. S.

Imperial College of Science and Technology,
South Kensington, S.W. 7

CONTENTS

LIST OF TABLES

LIST OF SYMBOLS

A Absorptivity; A_λ for wave-length λ, A_g of gas, A_s of surface, A_c o carbon dioxide, A_w of water vapour.

a Coefficient of volumetric expansion (for perfect gas $= 1/T$).

C Constant, dimensionless; C_H heat transfer factor, C_f friction factor.

c Specific heat per unit mass at constant pressure, B.Th.U./lb. °F.

d Diameter or thickness.

E Emissivity; E_λ for wave-length λ, E_g of gas, E_s of surface, E_c of carbon dioxide, E_w of water vapour, E_ϕ at angle ϕ.

e Base of hyperbolic, or natural, logarithms.

F Frictional force per unit area of surface, lb. $\times g$/ft.^{2} $=$ lb./ft. hr.^{2}

f Friction factor, dimensionless.

g Acceleration due to gravity, usually $4 \cdot 17 \times 10^8$ ft./hr.^{2}

H Heat transfer, B.Th.U./ft.^{2} hr.; H_l per unit length B.Th.U./ft. hr.

h Height, ft.

I Intensity of normal radiation, B.Th.U./ft.^{2} hr.

J Mechanical equivalent of heat, 778 ft. lb./B.Th.U.

j Electrical conductivity $= 1$/specific resistance.

k Thermal conductivity, B.Th.U./ft. hr. °F.

l Length, ft.

M Mass velocity $= v\rho$, lb./ft.^{2} hr. In pipe $= w/\pi r^2$. $M_{\max} =$ mass velocity at narrowest cross-section, $M_l =$ mass flow of condensate per unit length of horizontal pipe or per unit perimeter of vertical pipe in lb./ft. hr.

m Mass, lb.

n Number, e.g. of rows in pipe banks.

P Perimeter, ft.

p Pressure, lb./ft.^{2} unless otherwise stated; p_c partial pressure of carbon dioxide, in atmospheres; p_w partial pressure of water-vapour, in atmospheres; p_c critical pressure, lb./in.^{2}

Q Quantity of heat, B.Th.U.

q Latent heat of vaporization, B.Th.U./lb.

R Reflectivity, i.e. fraction of incident radiation reflected.

r Radius, ft. unless otherwise stated.

S Surface area, ft.^{2}

s Specific heat per unit volume at constant pressure, B.Th.U./ft.^{3} °F.

T Temperature, °F. absolute $= (t+460)$; T_s of surface, T_g of gas. Used also for transmission in Chapter I.

t Temperature, °F.; t_s of surface, t_g of gas, t_f of film, t_m mean temperature.

U Overall coefficient of heat transfer, B.Th.U./ft.^{2} hr. °F.

V Volume, ft.^{3}.

v Velocity, ft./hr. unless otherwise stated; v_{max} velocity corresponding to narrowest cross-section in pipe banks, v_s velocity of propagation of sound waves of small amplitude.

w Mass rate of flow, lb./hr. For flow inside pipe $= \pi r^2 M = \pi r^2 v \rho$.

X Centre to centre pipe spacing in tube banks in direction of flow. Expressed in terms of outer diameter of pipe, d.

Y Centre to centre pipe spacing in tube banks at right angles to direction of flow. Expressed in terms of outer diameter of pipe, d.

α Heat transfer coefficient, B.Th.U./ft.^{2} hr. °F.

δ Thickness of fluid layer.

ϵ Coefficient of emission.

θ Temperature difference, degs. F.

λ Wave-length.

μ Viscosity, lb./ft. hr.

ν Kinematic viscosity, ft.^{2}/hr $= \mu/\rho$.

ρ Density, lb./ft.^{3}

σ Surface tension, lb./ft.

τ Time, in hours unless otherwise stated.

ϕ Angle.

ω Solid angle.

DIMENSIONLESS 'GROUPS' OR 'NUMBERS' USED IN HEAT TRANSFER, ALL DIMENSIONLESS

Gr Grashof number $= ag\theta l^3 \rho^2/\mu^2$.

Gz Graetz number $= \omega c/kl$.

Ma Mach number $= v/v_s$.

Nu Nusselt number $= Hl/k\theta$.

$Pé$ Péclet number $= Re \times Pr = v\rho cl/k$.

Pr Prandtl number $= c\mu/k$.

Re Reynolds number $= v\rho l/\mu = Ml/\mu$.

St Stanton number $= Nu/(Re\ Pr) = H/c\theta v\rho$.

F.° denotes a temperature difference in degrees Fahrenheit.

I

RADIATION

ALL matter constantly emits thermal radiation, the rate of emission and the wave-length distribution depending upon the nature and temperature of the matter.

In general, when radiation falls on any body a fraction A is absorbed, a fraction R reflected, and a fraction T transmitted, so that

$$R+A+T = 1. \tag{1}$$

If the body is very thick, or nearly opaque,

$$R+A = 1 \quad \text{and} \quad A = 1-R, \tag{2}$$

the absorptivity being dependent only upon the reflectivity.

Fortunately most industrial materials, such as metals, refractories, brickwork, wood, or even glass for long wave-length heat radiation, are opaque enough for the transmission to be practically negligible, even for very small thicknesses, so that absorptivity, and as will be seen later emissivity also, can be considered simply as surface effects.

Reflectivity. When a surface is so smooth that its inequalities are small compared with the wave-length of the incident radiation, the angle of reflection is equal to the angle of incidence, i.e. the reflection is 'regular', and the reflectivity depends only upon the nature of the material and the wave-length of the incident radiation. But rough surfaces reflect 'diffusely' at all angles (although there may still be some preferential reflection at an angle equal to the angle of incidence), and the reflectivity depends upon the degree of roughness as well as upon the nature of the material and the wave-length of the incident radiation. Reflectivity can thus be altered by roughening, scratching, painting, oxidizing, or by other surface treatment.

The perfectly black body. In the limit, when a body reflects and transmits none of the incident radiation, whatever its wave-length, but absorbs it all, it is known as a perfectly black body, and its absorptivity is expressed as unity, the absorptivity of actual surfaces being expressed as a ratio to that of a black body.

B

Now it is a well-established experimental fact, confirmed by theory, that the better an absorber of radiant energy a surface is, the better emitter it will also be, and a perfectly black body not only absorbs all the radiation falling upon it, whatever its wave-length, but it also, at any given temperature, emits in every wave-length the maximum possible radiation for that tempera-ture. For this reason a black body is taken as a standard with which the emission from other bodies is compared, the emissivity of any actual surface in any given wave-length being defined as the ratio of the radiation which it emits in that wave-length to the radiation emitted in the same wave-length by a black body at the same temperature. In engineering problems it is usually the total emission in all wave-lengths which is of interest, and in general the term 'emissivity' is taken to mean the ratio of the total radia-tion emitted in all wave-lengths to the total radiation emitted in all wave-lengths by a black body at the same temperature.

Kirchhoff's law. According to Kirchhoff's law, for any given wave-length the ratio of the emissivity E_λ of any body to its absorptivity A_λ is the same for all bodies, and is equal to 1, i.e. to the emissivity of a black body in the same wave-length.

Thus $$\frac{E_\lambda}{A_\lambda} = 1 \quad \text{and} \quad E_\lambda = A_\lambda. \tag{3}$$

It follows that the total emissivity E in all wave-lengths of any given surface at any given temperature is equal to its total absorptivity A in all wave-lengths for radiation from a black body at that temperature.

Distribution of radiation among different wave-lengths. The total energy emitted by unit area of a black body in unit time depends only upon its temperature. Moreover, for any given temperature the distribution of the emitted radiation among the different wave-lengths is fixed. It will be seen from the curves in Fig. 1 that for any given temperature there is a peak in the distribution curve, corresponding to the wave-lengths emitted most strongly. As the temperature is increased, the radiation in every wave-length increases in intensity, but not in the same proportion. The peak shifts towards the region of shorter wave-lengths and becomes sharper. Below about 900° F. or 1,000° F. practically the whole of the emission is in waves too long to be recognized by the human eye as light. At about 1,000° F. the first visible red appears, and, as the

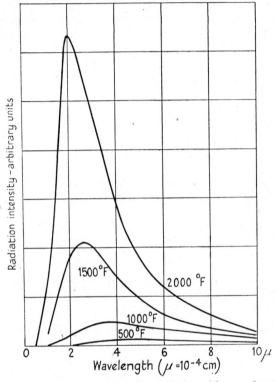

Fig. 1. Variation of black body radiation with wave-length.

temperature is further increased, the colour changes through dull red to cherry, orange, and white. A rough guess at the temperature of a body can be made from the colour and intensity of the radiation it emits, and experienced furnace workers can often make fairly reliable estimates in this way so long as the temperature is not too high.

Wien's law. Wien in 1896 found that the wave-length λ_{max} corresponding to the peak of the distribution curve for a black emitter is inversely proportional to the absolute temperature T

of the emitting body. If the temperature is expressed in °F. Abs., $\lambda_{max} T = 0.52$. If the temperature is in °C. Abs., $\lambda_{max} T = 0.29$, the wave-length being in centimetres in both cases.

Wien also found that the intensity of the emitted radiation at the peak wave-length is proportional to the fifth power of the absolute temperature of the emitting body. These laws can be applied to other wave-lengths, as well as to λ_{max}, so that, given the complete black body distribution curve for any one temperature, the curves for other temperatures can be deduced.

The Stefan-Boltzmann law. According to the well-known Stefan-Boltzmann law, the total rate at which energy is emitted in all wave-lengths by a black body is proportional to the fourth power of its absolute temperature. If the temperature is in °F. Abs.,

$$H = 1.73 \times 10^{-9} T^4 \text{ B.Th.U./ft.}^2 \text{ hr.} \qquad (4\,a)$$

If the temperature is in °C. Abs.,

$$H = 1.37 \times 10^{-12} T^4 \text{ cal./cm.}^2 \text{ sec.,} \qquad (4\,b)$$

the constant in these expressions being known as the Stefan-Boltzmann constant. For the purposes of heat transfer calculations this is the most important fundamental law of radiation. Values of $1.73 \times 10^{-9} T^4$ for a range of t from $10°$ F. to $3,000°$ F. are given in Table XV.

Emissivity and absorptivity of industrial surfaces. Perfect blackness is unattainable in practice, though certain substances such as platinum black and lampblack come very near it. In general the emission from any actual surface is not only less in every wave-length than that from a black body at the same temperature, but the ratio E_λ varies with the wave-length. Actual surfaces are thus 'selective' emitters, and their emissivity, i.e. the ratio of the total energy emitted in all wave-lengths to the total energy emitted in all wave-lengths by a black body at the same temperature, varies with the temperature. As we have already seen, the absorptivity A, of any surface, for radiation from a black body at any given temperature is equal to its emissivity at the same temperature. Absorptivity will thus vary with the temperature of the source from which the radiation is received.

Considering the almost unlimited variety of surfaces it is not surprising that measurements of emissivity are still very incomplete, but such results as are to be had are given in Table XVI. Some of these have been deduced from measurements of the diffuse reflectivity of surfaces for radiation in a narrow band of wave-lengths, and in such cases the values have been tabulated at the temperature for which the peak emission is in the wavelength band. Moreover, in determining emissivity, the radiation has, as a rule, been measured in a direction normal to the surface, and the assumption made that this gives the same result as if the total hemispherical radiation in all directions had been measured. But both E. Schmidt and Eckert [1] and Davisson and Weeks [2] found that the hemispherical emissivity of bright metals might be 18 to 20 per cent. above the normal emissivity, whereas for non-metallic surfaces it is usually slightly less than the normal emissivity.

Again, in deducing absorptivity from emissivity, no account is taken of possible variations of absorptivity with the temperature of the absorbing surface; about this, however, little is known.

For these and other reasons discretion must be used in applying the values given in the table. For instance, the emissivity of a molten metal at any temperature would obviously not be correctly obtained by difference from the reflectivity of the solid metal for radiation of the same range; and the values tabulated for white paper or other materials above their ignition point can obviously be applied only to absorptivity or reflectivity, and not to emissivity. A further difficulty is that industrial surfaces cannot usually be exactly specified, say if they are scratched, oxidized, rough, or dirty.

It should be noted that at temperatures below about 400° F. most non-metallic surfaces, whatever their colour, have emissivities not far from 0·9, but that as the temperature is increased the emissivities of the lighter coloured surfaces as a rule decrease. Dead black surfaces, such as lampblack, platinum black, or camphor soot, are nearly black body emitters at all temperatures. The emissivity of most polished metal surfaces, on the other hand, is very low at all temperatures, having, according to the electromagnetic theory, an inverse relation to their electrical conductivity, and increasing with temperature. Thus, note the relatively very high emissivity of polished bismuth, which has also a relatively very low electrical conductivity.

Attention may also be drawn to the fact that admixture of a small percentage of a coloured oxide or pigment to a white one causes a quite disproportionate increase in the emissivity; and that even a very thin layer of oil or varnish greatly increases the emissivity of a poorly emitting surface, such as a bright metal.

FORMULAE FOR CALCULATING HEAT TRANSFER BY RADIATION

For simplicity, in deriving formulae for calculating heat transfer by radiation, it is customary to take an imaginary 'grey' body which, although in every wave-length it emits less radiation than a black body, has its emissivity reduced in the same proportion for all wave-lengths and all temperatures. A grey body would thus have the same emissivity at all temperatures, and the same absorptivity, equal to its emissivity, whatever the temperature or wave-length distribution of the incident radiation.

The simplest case of radiation is that of a grey body of emissivity E_1 and absolute temperature T_1 in black surroundings at absolute temperature T_2 which, by definition, reflect back none of the grey body radiation. The grey body emits $1 \cdot 73 \times 10^{-9} E_1 T_1^4$ B.Th.U./ft.² hr. and receives from the surroundings a flux of radiation $1 \cdot 73 \times 10^{-9} T_2^4$ B.Th.U./ft.² hr., of which, since for all temperatures $E_1 = A_1$, it absorbs a fraction E_1. The net radiation interchange H is thus given by

$$H = 1 \cdot 73 \times 10^{-9} E_1 (T_1^4 - T_2^4) \text{ B.Th.U./ft.}^2 \text{ hr.} \qquad (5)$$

This expression is still applicable for surroundings that are not black, provided the radiating body is so small that it intercepts only a negligible proportion of the radiation reflected from the surroundings.

For a selective emitter, the absorptivity A_{1T_2} of the surface at T_1 for radiation from the surroundings at T_2 will not be equal to E_{1T_1}, its emissivity at T_1, but to E_{1T_2}, its emissivity at T_2. Hence (5) becomes

$$H = 1 \cdot 73 \times 10^{-9} (E_{1T_1} T_1^4 - E_{1T_2} T_2^4) \text{ B.Th.U./ft.}^2 \text{ hr.} \qquad (6)$$

At the other extreme, when all the radiation reflected from the surroundings is intercepted by the radiating body at T_1, as in the case of parallel planes large compared with their distance apart, or of concentric cylinders or spheres when the inner surface of outer cylinder or sphere is a regular reflector, it can easily be shown [3] that the appropriate expression for grey surfaces of temperature T_1 and T_2, and corresponding emissivities E_1 and E_2, is

$$H = 1 \cdot 73 \times 10^{-9} \frac{E_1 E_2}{E_1 + E_2 - E_1 E_2} (T_1^4 - T_2^4) \text{ B.Th.U./ft.}^2 \text{ hr.,} \quad (7)$$

or, for selective emitters, if A_{1T_2} is the absorptivity of the surface at T_1 for radiation from the surface at T_2, and A_{2T_1} the absorptivity of the surface at T_2 for radiation from the surface at T_1:

$$H = 1 \cdot 73 \times 10^{-9} \left[E_{1T_1} T_1^4 \left(\frac{A_{2T_1}}{A_{2T_1} + E_{1T_1}(1 - A_{2T_1})} \right) - \right.$$
$$\left. - E_{2T_2} T_2^4 \left(\frac{A_{1T_2}}{A_{1T_2} + E_{2T_2}(1 - A_{1T_2})} \right) \right] \frac{\text{B.Th.U.}}{\text{ft.}^2 \text{ hr.}}. \quad (8)$$

If both surfaces are of the same material so that $E_{1T_1} = A_{2T_1}$ and $E_{2T_2} = A_{1T_2}$, (8) reduces to

$$H = 1 \cdot 73 \times 10^{-9} \left[E_{1T_1} T_1^4 \frac{1}{(2 - E_{1T_1})} - E_{2T_2} T_2^4 \frac{1}{(2 - E_{2T_2})} \right] \frac{\text{B.Th.U.}}{\text{ft.}^2 \text{ hr.}}, \quad (9)$$

or if $E_{1T_1} = A_{1T_2}$, and $E_{2T_2} = A_{2T_1}$, i.e. if the surfaces are grey, it reduces to (7).

It can be proved [3] that for concentric cylinders, if the surfaces are grey, and if the inner surface of the outer cylinder reflects diffusely, the net radiation per unit area of the smaller cylinder is given by

$$H = 1 \cdot 73 \times 10^{-9} \frac{E_1 E_2}{E_2 + E_1(1 - E_2)(r_1/r_2)} (T_1^4 - T_2^4) \frac{\text{B.Th.U.}}{\text{ft.}^2 \text{ hr.}}, \quad (10)$$

where r_1 and r_2 are the radii of the inner and outer cylinders respectively. For concentric spheres a similar expression holds, except that r_1/r_2 must be replaced by r_1^2/r_2^2.

It will be seen that as r_1/r_2 decreases (10) tends to approach (5) so long as the outer cylinder or sphere is not too good a reflector. As r_1/r_2 increases (10) approaches (7), the expression for plane parallel surfaces, in which it should be noted that E_1 and E_2 occur symmetrically.

For concentric cylinders, if the surfaces are selective emitters, (10) becomes

$$H = 1.73 \times 10^{-9} \left[\frac{E_{1T_1} A_{2T_1} T_1^4}{A_{2T_1} + E_{1T_1}(1 - A_{2T_1})(r_1/r_2)} - \frac{E_{2T_2} A_{1T_2} T_2^4}{E_{2T_2} + A_{1T_2}(1 - E_{2T_2})(r_1/r_2)} \right] \frac{\text{B.Th.U.}}{\text{ft.}^2 \text{ hr.}} \quad (11)$$

assuming that the absorptivity of surface 1 for its own radiation reflected from surface 2 is equal to E_{1T_1}; and that the absorptivity of surface 1 for radiation from surface 2 is equal to A_{1T_2}, its absorptivity for radiation from a black body at T_2. Similarly for the absorptivities of surface 2.

In general the grey body formulae can be used without much error, even for surfaces with a relatively rapid rate of variation of emissivity with temperature, unless the temperatures are high and the temperature difference small. For instance, take a white refractory with emissivity 0·40 at 2,000° F., 0·70 at 1,000° F., and 0·90 at 100° F. At 2,000° F. in surroundings at 1,900° F., (5) would give results about 75 per cent. higher than (6): in surroundings at 1,100° F. results about 20 per cent. higher. But at 1,000° F. in surroundings at 900° F. the results given by (5) would be only about 15 per cent. high; in surroundings at 100° F. they would be practically correct.

For the parallel surfaces formulae (7) and (8) the differences are more complicated to work out, but if both the surfaces were of the same white refractory they would be very roughly twice those shown above.

Intensity of normal radiation I. The radiation from a small plane surface is, of course, strongest in the normal direction, and the intensity of normal radiation I is defined as the radiation emitted per unit time per unit surface area, per unit solid angle, from a small surface dS within a small cone of solid angle $d\omega$ with the normal as axis.

The intensity defined in a similar manner emitted in any

oblique direction, making an angle ϕ with the normal, is $I \cos \phi$.

The radiation from a small surface dS, through a small solid angle $d\omega$, making an angle ϕ with the normal is

$$I \, dS d\omega \cos \phi. \tag{12}$$

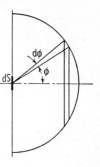

If two radial lines at angles ϕ and $\phi + d\phi$ to the normal rotate about the normal, they describe a solid angle $2\pi \sin \phi \, d\phi$. The radiation through this solid angle will be $I \, dS \, 2\pi \sin \phi \, d\phi \cos \phi$ and the total radiation in all forward directions will be

$$2\pi I \, dS \int_0^{\frac{1}{2}\pi} \sin \phi \cos \phi \, d\phi$$

$$= 2\pi I \, dS [\tfrac{1}{2} \sin^2\phi]_0^{\frac{1}{2}\pi} = \pi I \, dS \text{ B.Th.U./hr.} \tag{13}$$

But if the emissivity of the surface is E and its temperature T, the total radiation in all forward directions is also given by $1 \cdot 73 \times 10^{-9} E T^4 \, dS$ B.Th.U./hr., and therefore

$$I = \frac{1 \cdot 73 \times 10^{-9} E T^4}{\pi} \text{ B.Th.U./ft.}^2 \text{ hr.} \tag{14}$$

and the radiation through a small solid angle $d\omega$ is

$$\frac{1 \cdot 73 \times 10^{-9} E T^4}{\pi} \times dS d\omega \cos \phi \text{ B.Th.U./hr.} \tag{15}$$

Heat transfer by radiation between two small surfaces.

If a second small surface of area dS_2, grey emissivity E_2, and temperature T_2 is situated at a distance x from a surface of area dS_1, grey emissivity E_1, and temperature T_1, the normals to dS_1 and dS_2 being inclined at angles ϕ_1 and ϕ_2 to the line joining their centres, the small solid angle $d\omega$ which dS_2 subtends at dS_1 is equal to $dS_2 \cos \phi_2 / x^2$; hence the radiation from dS_1 which is absorbed by dS_2 is given by

$$E_2 I \, dS_1 \, d\omega \cos \phi_1 = \frac{1 \cdot 73 \times 10^{-9} E_1 E_2 \, dS_1 \, dS_2 \cos \phi_1 \cos \phi_2 \, T_1^4}{\pi x^2}.$$

This expression is symmetrical in dS_1 and dS_2, and their associated quantities, and therefore when T_1 is replaced by T_2 it represents the radiation emitted by dS_2 and absorbed by dS_1.

By subtraction, the net interchange of radiation between dS_1 and dS_2 is therefore equal to

$$\frac{1\cdot73\times10^{-9}}{\pi x^2} E_1 E_2 \, dS_1 \, dS_2 \cos\phi_1 \cos\phi_2 (T_1^4 - T_2^4) \text{ B.Th.U./hr.} \quad (16)$$

(16) refers only to the interchange of radiant energy between dS_1 and dS_2. If other surfaces are present in the neighbourhood, they must be included in a similar manner in calculating the net radiation transfer to or from any particular surface.

For example, suppose that dS_1 denotes the area of a small aperture in a furnace door and dS_2 that of a thermopile designed to measure the intensity of radiation from the furnace. The net rate at which the thermopile receives radiant energy from the aperture is given by (16). The thermopile also loses energy to the surrounding walls of the room or enclosure in which it is situated, and the temperature which it attains is determined by the condition that rates of gain and loss of energy shall be equal. If the area dS_1 subtends only a small angle at dS_2, the radiation from dS_2 to the surroundings at T_3 is given by $1\cdot73\times10^{-9}E_2 \, dS_2(T_2^4-T_3^4)$ B.Th.U./hr., or by twice this if both sides are exposed. By observing the temperature T_2 attained by the thermopile, the furnace temperature T_1 may be deduced, provided that the relative sizes, positions, and emissivities of dS_1 and dS_2 are known.

For finite surfaces the interchange of radiation may be obtained by integration, provided the surfaces are assumed to be black, i.e. that no reflected radiation is received by either surface from the other, E_1 and E_2 in (16) both being equal to unity. The results are conveniently expressed in terms of a geometric or angle factor.

Geometric factor. The geometric factor is defined as that fraction of the total radiation from a surface of area S_1 which is intercepted by another surface of area S_2, and depends only on the geometrical conditions.

If both surfaces are black, the radiation intercepted by S_2

from S_1 at absolute temperature T_1 will be $F_{12}S_1 \times 1 \cdot 73 \times 10^{-9}T_1^4$ B.Th.U./hr. Similarly, the radiation from S_2 at absolute temperature T_2 intercepted by S_1 will be $F_{21}S_2 \times 1 \cdot 73 \times 10^{-9}T_2^4$ B.Th.U./hr. The radiation interchange between the two surfaces will thus be

$$F_{12}S_1 \times 1 \cdot 73 \times 10^{-9}T_1^4 - F_{21}S_2 \times 1 \cdot 73 \times 10^{-9}T_2^4 \text{ B.Th.U./hr.}$$

If $T_1 = T_2$, the above expression will become equal to zero: hence $F_{12}S_1 = F_{21}S_2$, and the interchange of radiation can be expressed in terms of one area and one geometric factor, being given by

$$F_{12}S_1 \times 1 \cdot 73 \times 10^{-9}(T_1^4 - T_2^4)$$
$$= F_{21}S_2 \times 1 \cdot 73 \times 10^{-9}(T_1^4 - T_2^4) \text{ B.Th.U./hr.} \quad (17)$$

If a number of surfaces, 1, 2, 3,..., n, form an enclosure, all the radiation from any one surface, say surface 1, will be intercepted by the other surfaces, so that $F_{11} + F_{12} + F_{13} + ... + F_{1n} = 1$, where F_{11} is the fraction of the radiation from surface 1 intercepted by itself, which is zero for a flat or convex surface.

Calculation of geometric factors. The integrations involved in determining geometric factors are in general tedious, and the reader is referred elsewhere for solutions [4]. Only two simple cases will be considered here, to illustrate the method.

Geometric factor for two black surfaces lying entirely on a sphere of radius r. Let S_1 and S_2 be the spherical areas of the two surfaces and dS_1 and dS_2 elements of these surfaces at P_1 and P_2 respectively. Let I be the uniform intensity of normal radiation from S_1. The radiation from dS_1 which is intercepted by dS_2 is given by $I \cos\phi_1 \cos\phi_2 \, dS_1 dS_2 / P_1 P_2^2$, where ϕ_1 and ϕ_2 denote the angles made with $P_1 P_2$ by the normals to the surface at P_1 and P_2 respectively. Since $\cos\phi_1 = \cos\phi_2 = P_1 P_2 / 2r$ (see diagram), this becomes $I \, dS_1 dS_2 / 4r^2$, and by integration the radiation from S_1 intercepted by S_2 is $IS_1 S_2 / 4r^2$. The total radiation from S_1 is $\pi I S_1$, whence the proportion of the total radiation from S_1 which is intercepted by S_2, i.e. the geometric factor,

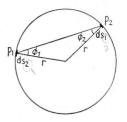

$$F_{12} = S_2 / 4\pi r^2, \quad (18)$$

i.e. F_{12} is equal to the ratio of the area S_2 to the total surface area of the sphere, and is independent of the positions of S_1 and S_2; or, in other words, the radiation from S_1 falls uniformly over the surface of the sphere. The surface S_1 absorbs a proportion $F_{11} = S_1/4\pi r^2$ of its own radiation.

Geometric factor for two black disks circumscribed by a sphere. Let S_1' and S_2' be the areas of the two disks, and r the

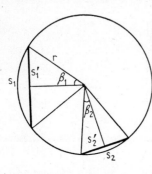

radius of an imaginary circumscribing sphere, and let S_1 and S_2 be the areas of the spherical caps cut off by S_1' and S_2'. The radiation from S_1' will be equal to that which would escape from a black spherical surface S_1 at the same temperature (see below), and, as shown above, will be uniformly distributed over the remainder of the sphere. Hence the proportion of the radiation from S_1' which is intercepted by S_2' or S_2 will be $S_2/(4\pi r^2 - S_1)$. If β_1 and β_2 are the semi-vertical angles of cones subtended at the centre of the sphere by S_1' and S_2' (see diagram), it can be shown that

$$F_{12} = S_2/(4\pi r^2 - S_1) = \sin^2\frac{\beta_2}{2}\bigg/\cos^2\frac{\beta_1}{2}. \qquad (19)$$

General case of radiation exchange between two surfaces. Since actual surfaces are never truly black, the net exchange of radiation between any two surfaces would always be below that given by (17), owing to successive reflections and absorptions. For non-black surfaces large compared with their distance apart, calculations of radiation interchange are usually very complicated, but for surfaces so small compared with their distance apart that the cosine of the angle between the line joining their centres and the line joining the centre of either to the edge of the other does not differ appreciably from unity, (16) is applicable.

Effect of indentations upon the radiation from a surface. A flat or convex surface emits radiation in proportion to its surface area. A concave surface, however, intercepts some of its

own radiation, which may suffer a number of successive reflections, and consequent reductions in intensity, before it can escape:
hence it emits less than a flat surface of the same total area.

If the edge of an indentation is in a single plane, and the surface
black, the emission from the mouth of the indentation will be
the same as that from a plane surface with the same edge; that
this is true is evident by considering the indentation and the
plane surface closing its mouth as together forming a uniform
temperature enclosure, each absorbing all the radiation falling

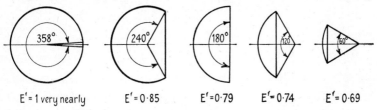

| $E' = 1$ very nearly | $E' = 0.85$ | $E' = 0.79$ | $E' = 0.74$ | $E' = 0.69$ |

FIG. 2. Effective emissivity of cavities forming part of sphere, $E = 0.65$.

upon it from the other. If, however, the surface of the indentation is not black, some of its own radiation will be intercepted
and reflected, and the emission will be greater than that from
a similar plane surface with the same edge. In the extreme case
of an enclosure which is complete, but for a very small aperture,
the emission from the aperture approaches closely that from
a black surface equal in area to the aperture and at the same
temperature as the enclosure. This provides a convenient method
of obtaining black body radiation experimentally.

In the special case of an indentation whose surface forms part
of a sphere, the effective emissivity E' (i.e. the ratio of the emission to that from a black surface of the same shape, size, and
temperature) is given by

$$E' = \frac{E}{1 - \dfrac{S(1-E)}{4\pi r^2}}, \tag{20}$$

where S = area of curved surface,

             r = radius of curvature of surface,

             E = surface emissivity.

Values of E' for spherical caps, $E = 0.65$, are shown in Fig. 2.

EXAMPLE 1

A metal storage tank of external area 6 ft.² containing water at 150° F. is in a large enclosure with walls at 50° F. The tank is painted dead black on the outside, so that its emissivity is 0·95. By how much would the heat loss from it be reduced if it were coated with aluminium paint of emissivity 0·55?

Solution. Since the tank is small compared with its surroundings, and is not at a high temperature, expression (5) holds.

The heat loss from the black surface would thus be

$$6 \times 1·73 \times 10^{-9} \times 0·95[(150+460)^4 - (50+460)^4] \text{ B.Th.U./hr.}$$

and from the bright surface

$$6 \times 1·73 \times 10^{-9} \times 0·55[(150+460)^4 - (50+460)^4] \text{ B.Th.U./hr.}$$

The saving would thus be

$$6 \times 1·73 \times 10^{-9} \times (0·95-0·55)[(150+460)^4 - (50+460)^4]$$
$$\text{B.Th.U./hr.,}$$

which, from Table XV,

$$= 6 \times 0·40 \times (240-117) = 295 \text{ B.Th.U./hr.}$$

EXAMPLE 2

A metal rod of diameter $\frac{1}{2}$ in. runs along the axis of a cylindrical furnace of inner diameter 8 in., the inner surfaces of which are kept at 1,600° F. The absorptivity of the rod is 0·60, its density is 500 lb./ft.³, and its specific heat is 0·14 B.Th.U./lb. °F. How long would the rod take to heat from 800° F. to 850° F.?

Solution. Since the rod is small compared with its surroundings, and the temperature difference comparatively large, the radiation it absorbs can be calculated from expression (5) and will be given by:

(a) $1·73 \times 10^{-9} \times 0·60[(1600+460)^4 - (800+460)^4]$

B.Th.U./ft.² hr. at the beginning of the period.

(b) $1·73 \times 10^{-9} \times 0·60[(1600+460)^4 - (850+460)^4]$

B.Th.U./ft.² hr. at the end of the period.

From Table XV

(a) $= 0·6(31100-4360) = 16040 \text{ B.Th.U./ft.}^2 \text{ hr.}$

(b) $= 0·6(31100-5090) = 15610 \text{ B.Th.U./ft.}^2 \text{ hr.}$

These are so nearly the same that the mean value, 15800 B.Th.U./ ft.^{2} hr., can be taken.

Surface area of rod per ft. length $= \pi/24$ ft.^{2}

$\therefore$ Heat absorbed per ft. length $= 15800 \times \pi/24$

$$= 660\pi \text{ B.Th.U./hr.}$$

Heat capacity of rod per ft. length $= \dfrac{\pi}{48 \times 48} \times 500 \times 0.14$

$$= \dfrac{70\pi}{48 \times 48} \text{ B.Th.U./}^\circ\text{F.}$$

$\therefore$ Heat required to raise temp. 50 degrees $= \dfrac{50 \times 70\pi}{48 \times 48}$ B.Th.U.

$\therefore$ Time required $= \dfrac{3500\pi}{48 \times 48 \times 660\pi}$ hours

$$= \dfrac{3500 \times 60 \times 60}{48 \times 48 \times 660} \text{ seconds} = 8.3 \text{ seconds.}$$

EXAMPLE 3

A dead black cylinder of emissivity 0.95 is kept at 200° F. in a large enclosure at 50° F. Find the radiation lost per square foot of its surface.

What would the radiation loss become if the cylinder were surrounded by a concentric cylinder with its inner surface of brightly polished metal, emissivity 0.10?

Solution. For the freely exposed cylinder the radiation loss will be

$$1.73 \times 10^{-9} \times 0.95[(200+460)^4 - (50+460)^4] \text{ B.Th.U./ft.}^2 \text{ hr.}$$

From Table XV this $= 0.95(328-117) = 200$ B.Th.U./ft.^{2} hr. For the concentric cylinders, since the inner surface of the outer cylinder is a regular reflector, the parallel planes formulae apply, and, since the absolute temperatures concerned are comparatively low, the grey body formula (7) may be used. Hence the radiation loss will be:

$$\frac{0.95 \times 0.10}{0.95 + 0.10 - (0.95 \times 0.10)}(328 - 117)$$

$$= 0.10(328 - 117) = 21 \text{ B.Th.U./ft.}^2 \text{ hr.}$$

It will be noticed that in this case, where one of the surfaces is nearly black, the effective emissivity is nearly equal to that of the other surface.

EXAMPLE 4

In the above example, calculate the corresponding radiation losses for an inner cylinder of emissivity 0·10.

Solution. For the freely exposed cylinder the radiation loss will now be

$$0\cdot10(328-117) = 21 \text{ B.Th.U./ft.}^2 \text{ hr.,}$$

that is, it will be the same as for the black cylinder surrounded by a cylinder of emissivity 0·10. When surrounded by a polished cylinder the radiation loss will become

$$\frac{0\cdot10\times0\cdot10}{0\cdot10+0\cdot10-(0\cdot10\times0\cdot10)}(328-117)$$

$$= 0\cdot053(328-117) = 11 \text{ B.Th.U./ft.}^2 \text{ hr.}$$

which is very low, as in a Thermos flask.

EXAMPLE 5

A white refractory material has emissivity 0·40 at 2,000° F. and 0·43 at 1,900° F. If a piece of the refractory at 1,900° F. were exposed to black furnace walls at 2,000° F., at what rate would it gain heat by radiation?

Solution. In this case, since the absolute temperatures concerned are high, expression (6) must be used. It allows for the fact that the absorptivity of the white refractory for radiation from a black body at 2,000° F. is equal to the emissivity of the refractory at 2,000° F. Hence the radiation the white refractory gains will be

$$1\cdot73\times10^{-9}\times0\cdot40(2000+460)^4-0\cdot43(1900+460)^4$$

$$\text{B.Th.U./ft.}^2 \text{ hr.}$$

which, from Table XV,

$$= (0\cdot40\times63300)-(0\cdot43\times53600) \text{ B.Th.U./ft.}^2 \text{ hr.}$$

$$= 25320-23050 = 2270 \text{ B.Th.U./ft.}^2 \text{ hr.}$$

If the grey body formula (5) had been used, an incorrect answer would have resulted:

$$= 0\cdot43(63300-53600) = 4170 \text{ B.Th.U./ft.}^2 \text{ hr.,}$$

which is 84 per cent. too high.

EXAMPLE 6

A thin metal disk of diameter 6 in., blackened on both sides, is exposed to the radiation from a normally opposed parallel disk of the same size, 3 ft. away, maintained at 1,000° F. If the surroundings are otherwise at 60° F., find the equilibrium temperature of the blackened disk, for simplicity taking its emissivity as 1, and neglecting heat loss from it by convection. The emissivity of the hot disk is 0·8.

Solution. The two disks may both be considered as 'small', in the sense that the angle subtended by either at the other is small. The radiation interchange between them will thus be given by (16), with $\cos\phi_1$ and $\cos\phi_2$ both equal to 1.

If the equilibrium temperature of the black disk is $T°$ F. Abs., its heat loss by radiation to the surroundings, remembering that it has two sides, will be $1·73\times10^{-9}\times2S(T^4-520^4)$ B.Th.U./hr., where S is the surface area of one side of the disk.

Hence, in equilibrium, when the heat it gains by radiation from the hot disk is just equal to the heat it loses by radiation to the surroundings:

$$\frac{1·73\times10^{-9}\times0·8\times S^2}{\pi\times3\times3}\times(1460^4-T^4)\ ,$$

$$=1·73\times10^{-9}\times2S\times(T^4-520^4),$$

whence

$$(4·54\times10^{12}-T^4)=\frac{(T^4-7·31\times10^{10})\times2\times9\times4\times4}{0·8}$$

$$=360(T^4-7·31\times10^{10})$$

and $T^4=8·56\times10^{10}$, whence $T=540°$ F. Abs. $=80°$ F.

Actually, since the disk would lose heat to the surroundings by convection at about the same rate as by radiation, the real equilibrium temperature would be approximately 70° F.

EXAMPLE 7

A blackened surface of area 1 ft.² and emissivity 1 is parallel to a gas-fire and 12 ft. away from it in a direction at 45° to the plane of the fire. It absorbs radiation from the fire at the rate of 7 B.Th.U./hr. If the fire burns gas of calorific value 500 B.Th.U./ft.³ at the rate of 30 ft.³/hr., and its effective area is $\frac{3}{4}$ ft.², what is its radiant efficiency?

C

Solution. From expression (12) the radiation falling on the blackened surface will be

$$I \, ds d\omega \cos\phi = 7 \text{ B.Th.U./hr.},$$

where I is the intensity of normal radiation, ds is the effective area of the fire $= \frac{3}{4}$ ft.^{2}, $d\omega$ the small solid angle subtended by the blackened surface at the gas-fire $= \cos\phi/(12 \times 12)$, and $\cos\phi = \cos 45° = 0.71$.

But the total radiation emitted by the fire, from expression (13),

$$= \pi I \, ds = 7\pi/d\omega \cos\phi = 7\pi \times 12 \times 12/\cos^2\phi$$
$$= 6340 \text{ B.Th.U./hr.}$$

The heat of the gas burned $= 500 \times 30 = 15000$ B.Th.U./hr. Hence the radiant efficiency $= 6340 \times 100/15000 = 42.5$ per cent.

GAS RADIATION

Gases with symmetrical molecules, such as hydrogen, nitrogen, and oxygen, or mixtures of these gases such as air, do not radiate appreciably even at high temperatures; nor do they absorb radiation passing through them. But the heteropolar gases such as water vapour, carbon dioxide, carbon monoxide, sulphur dioxide, ammonia, hydrocarbons, etc., may radiate strongly in certain limited bands of wave-length, which are different for the different gases. Of these, the only ones that have been the subject of systematic investigation are water vapour and carbon dioxide, which, since they are found in considerable proportions in products of combustion, are of great industrial importance.

Emissivity and absorptivity of partially transparent substances. In calculating the radiation from a gas layer, thickness as well as surface area must be taken into account. The degree to which a partially transparent material such as a gas absorbs radiation can be expressed in terms of its coefficient of absorption, a, for that radiation, of which in passing through a thickness x of the material, a fraction $(1 - e^{-ax})$ is absorbed and a fraction e^{-ax} transmitted, where e is the base of the hyperbolic logarithms.

Similarly it can be shown that a layer of gas of thickness x will emit

$$(\epsilon/a)(1 - R)(1 - e^{-ax}) \text{ per unit area,} \tag{21}$$

where ϵ is the coefficient of emission, i.e. the radiation emitted by unit volume in unit time. The corresponding radiation emitted by a black body, which neither transmits nor reflects, would be ϵ/a. Hence the emissivity of the layer, expressed as a ratio of black body emissivity, would be $(1-R)(1-e^{-ax})$. But this is evidently equal to the absorptivity, since when radiation falls upon the surface of the layer, of the fraction $(1-R)$ which penetrates it, a fraction $(1-e^{-ax})$ is absorbed. Hence, for a partially transparent material, emissivity in any wave-length or at any temperature is, as for opaque substances, equal to absorptivity for the same wave-length or for radiation from a black body at the same temperature.

According to the above, the radiation from a gas should increase exponentially with the number of radiating molecules in the thickness of the radiating layer, i.e. with pl where p is the partial pressure of the radiating gas and l the thickness of the gas layer. Knowing the bands of wave-length in which the gas radiates, and the corresponding coefficients of emission, it should thus be possible to calculate the emissivity. But attempts have shown that this is too complicated to be feasible, since not only must the radiation for the different characteristic bands be considered separately, but the coefficient of emission in any given band varies with the wave-length, and the wave-length limits of the bands are not exactly known. Moreover, in the case of a gas, the radiation may depend to some extent upon p and l separately as well as upon their product. It has also been found that the absorptivity of a gas may depend appreciably upon its own temperature as well as upon the temperature of the source of radiation. Hence for practical purposes the emissivity, and absorptivity, must be found experimentally.

Measurements of emissivity and absorptivity of gases. During the past few years a number of measurements of emissivity have been made, mainly for carbon dioxide and water vapour. Hottel and Egbert [5] have recently reviewed the existing data, from which they have deduced the best values. They consider that the error in the emissivity figures is less than 5 per cent., but the measurements of absorptivity are less accurate.

The emissivity, E, of a gas is usually given in a series of curves in which E is plotted against the temperature of the radiating gas for different values of the product pl of the partial pressure p, and the thickness of the gas layer, l, assumed the same in all directions. Actually, l is the same in all directions only for the artificial case of a hemisphere radiating to the mid-point of its base; for other shapes the radius of the hemisphere which would give the same emissivity has to be determined before values can be read from the curves. This has been calculated for a number of simple shapes, as shown in Table I. In the limit, as pl decreases,

TABLE I. *Equivalent Thickness l for Non-Luminous Gas Radiation Layers of Different Shapes*

Shape	Characteristic dimension Z	Factor by which Z is to be multiplied to give equivalent l for hemispherical radiation	
		Calculated by various workers	$3.4 \times$ (volume/area)
Sphere	Diameter	0·60	0·57
Cube	Side	0·60	0·57
Infinite cylinder radiating to walls	Diameter	0·90	0·85
Ditto, radiating to centre of base	Diameter	0·90	0·85
Cylinder, height = diameter, radiating to whole surface .	Diameter	0·60	0·57
Ditto, radiating to centre of base	Diameter	0·77	0·57
Space between infinite parallel planes	Distance apart	1·80	1·70
Space outside infinite bank of tubes with centres on equilateral triangles, tube diameter = clearance . .	Clearance	2·80	2·89
Ditto, but tube diameter = one-half clearance . .	Clearance	3·80	3·78
Ditto, with tube centres on squares, and tube diameter = clearance	Clearance	3·50	3·49
Rectangular parallelepiped, $1 \times 2 \times 6$ radiating to:	Shortest edge		
2 × 6 face . . .	,,	1·06	1·01
1 × 6 face . . .	,,	1·06	1·05
1 × 2 face . . .	,,	1·06	1·01
all faces	,,	1·06	1·02
Infinite cylinder of semicircular cross-section radiating to centre of flat side . .	Diameter	0·63	0·52

l becomes equal to $(4 \times \text{volume})/\text{area}$. For practical cases, l can be taken as $(3\cdot4 \times \text{volume})/\text{area}$ which usually gives a sufficiently accurate result.

Carbon dioxide and water vapour. Using the subscript c

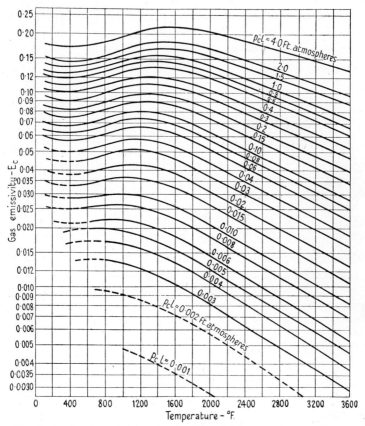

FIG. 3. Emissivity of carbon dioxide for total pressure 1 atmosphere.

for carbon dioxide and w for water vapour, the variation of the emissivity, E_c, with the partial pressure, p_c, for any given value of $p_c l$, is negligible, and emissivities for a total pressure of 1 atmosphere can be read off directly from the curves in Fig. 3. For water vapour, a correction must be applied for variation of the emissivity, E_w, with p_w for a given value of

$p_w l$. In this case the initial curves shown in Fig. 4 are plotted for the limiting case of $p_w = 0$, and subsidiary curves are given in Fig. 5 for finding the factor by which the values of E_w read from Fig. 4 must be multiplied to obtain corrected values

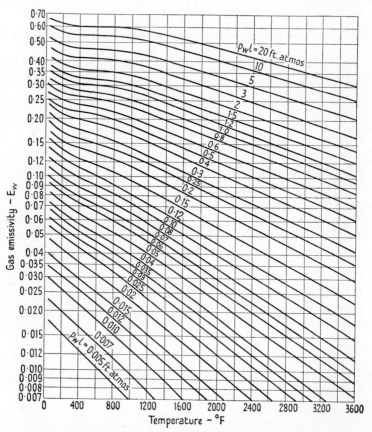

FIG. 4. Emissivity of water vapour for total pressure 1 atmosphere.

for any actual partial pressure. In calculating pl, p is to be expressed in atmospheres and l in feet.

It will be seen from Figs. 3 and 4 that for carbon dioxide E_c goes through a maximum at a temperature between 600° F. and 1,600° F. depending upon the value of $p_c l$, while for water vapour E_w decreases with increasing temperature throughout the range.

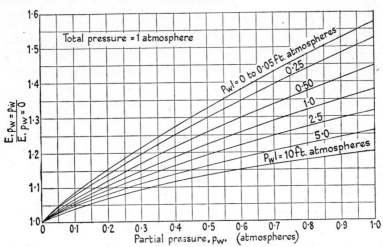

FIG. 5. Ratio of emissivity of water vapour for $p_w = p_w$
to that for $p_w = 0$.

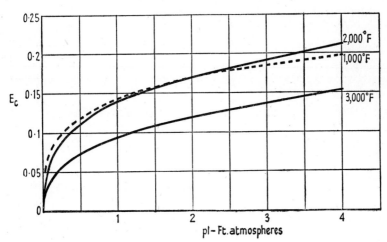

FIG. 6. Variation of emissivity of carbon dioxide with pl.

In Figs. 6 and 7 the emissivities, as read from Figs. 3 and 4, are shown for the two gases separately against the product pl, for temperatures of 1,000° F., 2,000° F., and 3,000° F. Except for small values of pl the emissivity of water vapour is higher than that of carbon dioxide; at 1,000° F., for $p_w l = 10$ at. ft. it is more than one-half that of a black body.

For a total pressure x, and a partial pressure p, atmospheres, E may be somewhat greater than for a total pressure 1 atmosphere, with pl increased to xpl, i.e. for the same number of mole-

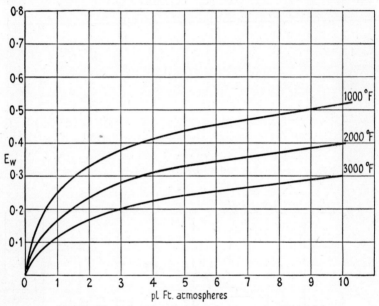

FIG. 7. Variation of emissivity of water vapour with pl.

cules: but not enough is yet known about the effects of total pressure upon E to allow for reliable corrections.

Since the emission bands of carbon dioxide and water vapour overlap, either gas is absorbent to radiation from the other. Thus, when both are present, the total radiation emitted is less than the sum of that due to the two gases separately. Hottel's curves for correcting for this effect are given in Fig. 8. They show, for different values of $p_w/(p_c+p_w)$, and for different values of $(p_c l+p_w l)$, the amount which must be subtracted from (E_c+E_w) to give E_{c+w}.

Values of absorptivity for radiation from boundary surfaces, assumed black, at any given temperature, can be obtained from the curves in a similar manner, provided that the gas is appreciably hotter than the enclosing surfaces and the absorption term consequently of secondary importance. But if the reverse is the case, and greater accuracy is needed, the values of $p_c l$ and $p_w l$ should be multiplied by T_s/T_g, where T_s and T_g are the surface and gas temperatures respectively, and the resulting products then used for finding E_c and E_w from Figs. 3 and 4. The emissivities thus obtained must then be

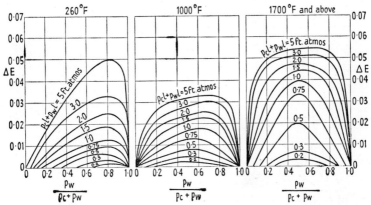

FIG. 8. Emissivity correction for mixtures of carbon dioxide and water vapour.

multiplied by $(T_g/T_s)^{0.65}$ for carbon dioxide and $(T_g/T_s)^{0.45}$ for water vapour.

Radiation from carbon monoxide. Flue gases often contain a proportion of carbon monoxide, though its radiation is usually small compared with that from other constituents. Ullrich [6] found that the emissivity of carbon monoxide is a maximum around 1,600° F. Between 600° F. and 2,500° F. its emission for $pl = 2$ is about half, and for $pl = 0.01$ varies from about 40 to 90 per cent., that of carbon dioxide.

Radiation from ammonia. The emissivity of ammonia gas, as measured by Port [7], is much higher than that of carbon dioxide or water vapour. In common with these gases it shows a decreasing emissivity with increasing temperature. Between room temperature and 2,000° F. Port [7] found values that at $pl = 2$ varied from once to twice those for water vapour, at

$pl = 0·01$ from one-and-a-half to four times those for water vapour.

Net radiation between a gas and its enclosure. In calculating the net radiation interchange between a radiating gas at T_g and black bounding surfaces at T_s the expression is

$$H = 1·73 \times 10^{-9}(E_g T_g^4 - A_g T_s^4) \text{ B.Th.U./ft.}^2 \text{ hr.,} \qquad (22)$$

where E_g is the emissivity of the gas at T_g and A_g its absorptivity for radiation from a black body at T_s.

If the emissivity of the boundaries is appreciably below 1, it must be taken into account, for in this case some of the gas radiation will be reflected at the boundaries, most of this passing unabsorbed through the gas and having a further opportunity of being absorbed at the boundaries. Similarly for the second and successive reflections. For most industrial applications a close enough approximation is given by introducing a factor

$$E_s' = (E_s + 1)/2$$

into (22). Indeed, in many actual problems, owing to uncertainties in the shape factor, the gas composition and the emissivity of the boundaries, and to unknown temperature variations in the gas mass, it is often not worth putting in any corrections at all.

When there is a continuous change in the temperatures of gas and surface along an interchanger, a good approximation is given by taking the arithmetic mean of the surface temperature and a gas temperature found by adding the logarithmic mean of the temperature differences θ_1 and θ_2 between gas and surface at the two ends to the mean surface temperature; that is,

$$T_g = T_s + (\theta_1 - \theta_2)/\log_e \frac{\theta_1}{\theta_2}. \qquad (23)$$

Again, it is sometimes convenient to write (22) as

$$H = 1·73 \times 10^{-9} E(T_g^4 - T_s^4) \text{ B.Th.U./ft.}^2 \text{ hr.,} \qquad (24)$$

where E is a 'grey' emissivity which gives the right result for H. It can be seen that E is equal to

$$\frac{E_g - A_g(T_s/T_g)^4}{1 - (T_s/T_g)^4}.$$

EXAMPLE

Flue gases containing 10 per cent. of carbon dioxide and 20 per cent. of water vapour enter a heavily insulated tube 3 ft. long and inner diameter 6 in. at 1,200° F. and leave at 1,000° F. The mean temperature of the tube wall is 900° F. and its emissivity 0·8. Neglecting convection, at what speed do the gases enter the tube? Their specific heat at 1,200° F. may be taken as 0·007 B.Th.U./ft.^{3} °F.

Solution. The radius of hemisphere equivalent to a 6-in. tube 3 ft. long is given by:

$$\frac{3\cdot4\times\text{volume}}{\text{area}} = \frac{3\cdot4\times\pi r^2 l}{2\pi rl+2\pi r^2} = \frac{1\cdot7rl}{(l+r)} = \frac{1\cdot7\times3}{4\times(13/4)} = 0\cdot4 \text{ ft.}$$

Hence, for CO_2, $p_c l = 0\cdot10\times0\cdot4 = 0\cdot04$ at. ft.,

for H_2O, $p_w l = 0\cdot20\times0\cdot4 = 0\cdot08$ at. ft.

Since the difference between inlet and outlet gas temperatures is not great the mean value may be taken as a close enough approximation, i.e. 1,100° F.

From Fig. 3, for $p_c l = 0\cdot04$ at. ft., the emissivities of CO_2 at 1,100° F. and 900° F. respectively are 0·057 and 0·055.

From Fig. 4, for $p_w l = 0\cdot08$ at. ft., and $p_w = 0$, the emissivities of H_2O at 1,100° F. and 900° F. respectively are 0·061 and 0·069. According to Fig. 5, for $p_w = 0\cdot20$, these need multiplying by 1·15, bringing them to 0·070 and 0·079 respectively.

Thus E_{c+w} for 1,100° F. and 900° F. respectively is equal to 0·127 and 0·134 respectively, since it will be seen from Fig. 8 that the correction for mutual absorption at such low values of $(p_c l+p_w l)$ is negligible.

Hence the net radiation from the gas to the tube walls will be given by

$$\frac{(0\cdot8+1)}{2} \times 1\cdot73\times 10^{-9}(0\cdot127\times 1560^4-0\cdot134\times 1360^4)$$

B.Th.U./ft.^{2} hr.

which (see Table XV) is equal to

$0\cdot9\times 10^5(0\cdot127\times 1\cdot02-0\cdot134\times 0\cdot59) = 454$ B.Th.U./ft.^{2} hr.

or, for the total area of the tube, to

$$\pi\times\tfrac{1}{2}\times3\times454 = 2140 \text{ B.Th.U./hr.}$$

If v is the inlet velocity in ft./hr., the volume of gas flowing is $\pi r^2 v$ ft.³/hr. and its heat capacity $0 \cdot 007 \pi r^2 v$ B.Th.U./°F. hr.

Hence v is given by

$$\frac{2140}{0 \cdot 007 \times \pi r^2 v} = 200,$$

whence $\quad v = \dfrac{2140 \times 7 \times 4 \times 4}{200 \times 0 \cdot 007 \times 22 \times 60 \times 60}$ ft./sec. $= 2 \cdot 2$ ft./sec.

If instead of inlet and outlet gas temperatures the inlet temperature and gas volume were known, a preliminary shot at finding the exit gas temperature would have to be made, and from this a more accurate value determined.

Suppose the gas throughout the tube were at 1,200° F., a calculation similar to the previous one shows that the heat transfer would be enough to drop the gas temperature by 334 degrees. Obviously this is too great, but taking the mean of no temperature drop, and 334 degrees drop = 167 degrees, we get a mean gas temperature of 1,200−(167/2) = 1,117° F. which would give enough heat transfer to cause a temperature drop of 223 degrees. Again taking the mean, i.e. of 167 and 223, we arrive at a temperature drop of 195 degrees and a mean gas temperature of 1,102° F. which is obviously near enough.

In this case, however, the calculations could have been simplified, and the same result obtained, by using (24) instead of (22), and assuming that over the possible range of gas temperature there was no appreciable variation in E.

Gas radiation in a furnace. As a rule, it is not merely the direct radiation interchange between gas and boundary walls that is in question. In most furnace problems there is direct interchange of radiation between the combustion gases and the charge, between the combustion gases and the furnace walls, and between the furnace walls and the charge. And both solid radiation and gas radiation are reflected and re-reflected from all parts of the furnace walls and charge to other parts, being partially absorbed by the gas at every passage through it. Two types of problem occur in practice: in the first type steady flow conditions prevail, as in a boiler; in the second, conditions are transient, as when a cold charge is introduced into a hot furnace. In either case it may generally be assumed that the furnace walls are heavily insulated, and the heat lost through them therefore relatively small.

When flow conditions are steady, the walls take up an equilibrium temperature, between the temperatures of the hot gas and the heat-receiving surface. To get a heat balance between heat supplied and heat absorbed would involve methods of trial and error, due allowance being made for convection if necessary. But, if the heat loss through the walls is assumed to be roughly balanced by convection from the hot gases to the walls, radiation from the gases falling on the walls which is reflected or re-radiated will increase the heat transfer to the receiving surface or charge. The total heat transfer by gas radiation, to an absorbing surface of area S, in the furnace, may then be considered as being equal to the heat transfer which would occur by direct gas radiation alone, to a surface of area $S+xS_R$, where x is a fraction and S_R is the total area of refractory walls, from which it is assumed there is no external loss. If S_R/S is large, x approaches zero, while if S_R/S and A_G are small, x approaches unity. For most practical cases, x will lie between 0·5 and 0·9 and generally a value of 0·7 gives a reasonable approximation.†

When a cold charge is inserted in a hot furnace a quite different state of affairs exists. Prior to putting cold material into the furnace there will usually be little temperature difference between the combustion gases and the inner walls of the furnace. But the introduction of the cold material will cause a sudden chilling of the furnace walls owing to the large initial temperature difference, and a consequent high rate of heat transfer from walls to charge, which gas radiation and convection to the walls fail to counterbalance. As the charge warms up, the temperature of the walls will rise again, and during this stage the walls receive more heat from the gases than they re-radiate to the charge. In due course the charge will attain some final constant temperature, between that of the hot gases and the walls, and at this stage all the temperature differences will be small, the only heat loss

† See McAdams, *Heat Transmission* (1942), p. 70.

being that required to balance conduction losses. Over the whole warming-up period the total amount of heat absorbed by the walls from the gases will be equal to the heat radiated to the charge from the walls, although at any particular instant this is not so.

RADIATION FROM CLOUDS OF PARTICLES

The radiation from hot suspended particles in a gas or flame depends essentially upon whether or not the particles are large enough to be opaque. Powdered coal flames contain particles varying in diameter from about 0·01 in. downwards, which may have any composition from nearly pure carbon to nearly pure ash. Many of them will be thick enough to be practically opaque. On the other hand, the particles suspended in luminous gas flames, which are caused by the decomposition of hydrocarbons, and consist of carbon or very heavy hydrocarbons, have an initial diameter of only about 0·00001 in. and transmit a considerable fraction of the radiation falling upon them.

The radiation from a cloud of non-reflecting opaque carbon particles can be calculated if their size and number per unit volume are known, but when the particles are partially transparent the calculation is too complicated to be manageable.

Radiation from a cloud of opaque particles. Rays from any single opaque particle in a cloud can escape only if they are not intercepted and absorbed by other particles. But, assuming a random distribution, the probability of the radiation from particles at different depths reaching the surface can be calculated, and the total radiation escaping found by summing the contributions from particles at different depths. This increases with the product nSd according to an exponential law, so that $E = 1 - e^{-nSd}$, where d is the thickness of the cloud, n the number of particles per unit volume, and S the mean cross-sectional area of the particles, which are assumed to be all at the same temperature. If the cloud is of such a shape that the length of path is different in different directions, the effective length for hemispherical radiation has to be determined as described previously for gas radiation.

Wohlenberg [8], Haslam and Hottel [9], and Lindmark [10], have given empirical expressions for the calculation of the radiation from pulverized coal flames of given type, but the validity of some of their assumptions is open to doubt. Sherman [11] made direct measurements of the radiation from several pulverized coal flames for a thickness of about 3 ft. and found that the emissivity varied from about 0·65 at a distance of $\frac{1}{2}$ ft. from the burner to 0·4 at a distance of $11\frac{1}{2}$ ft. from the burner, where much of the carbon had burned away. From the results he estimated the emissivities for greater thicknesses. For a flame thickness of 10 ft. he concluded that near the burner the emissivity would be almost 1, and that even 10 ft. or more from the burner it would still be above 0·8. For a flame thickness of 20 ft. E would be practically 1 throughout; this would apply to modern pulverized coal installations, where the flames are usually very big.

Sherman [11] found that the type of coal burned had more effect upon the radiation than the fineness, the quantity of excess air, or the rate of heat input. The importance of the radiation from the solid particles in a flame is shown by the fact that non-luminous gas flames in the same furnace gave emissivity about 0·2 as against 0·7 to 0·3 for the pulverized coal flames, according to the distance from the burner.

Radiation from a cloud of partially transparent particles: luminous flames. The emission even from a non-reflecting partially transparent particle is less than black-body emission. The radiation from a cloud of such particles thus depends upon the sizes and absorption coefficients of the individual particles, as well as upon their concentration. Since the absorption coefficient, as for gas radiation, varies with the wave-length, the problem becomes very complicated. The most important practical case is that of the luminous gas flame, the carbon particles in which transmit roughly 95 per cent. and absorb 5 per cent. of the thermal radiation incident upon them. The absorptivity, or emissivity, decreases with increase of wave-length, so that a luminous flame which to the eye appears opaque may be far from opaque for long-wave-length thermal radiations.

The emissivity of luminous gas flames may be much higher than that of non-luminous flames of the same temperature. For an acetylene flame, for instance, Haslam and Boyer [12] were able to increase the radiation 400 per cent. by luminosity, and Lent [13] made a blast-furnace flame almost black by adding benzene, which caused the formation of soot.

Sherman [14] measured the emissivity of natural gas burning in a furnace of diameter $3\frac{1}{2}$ ft. as non-luminous, semi-luminous, and luminous flames, with little or no excess air. The rate of heat input, about 3 million B.Th.U./hr., was the same in all cases. The values obtained were respectively about 0·20, 0·25, and 0·60, but the corresponding differences in the radiation emitted were partially counterbalanced by the temperatures decreasing as the luminosity increased. The radiation from the semi-luminous flame was thus much the same as that from the non-luminous, but the fully luminous flame gave much more radiation. In an actual furnace, however, where the charge is receiving heat from the walls as well as from the gases, the absorption by the luminous gases of radiation from the furnace walls, which is thus cut off from the charge, may offset the greater radiation from the gases themselves. In Sherman's furnace the radiation from flame and wall together was actually greater for the non-luminous than for the luminous flames, and he concluded that in furnaces where the roof and walls are at a higher temperature than the work to be heated the possibility of increasing the rate of heat transfer by increasing the luminosity of the flame is limited. But in boiler furnaces with water-cooled walls, where no high-temperature solid radiating surfaces are found, increasing the emissivity of the flame would have greater effect.

'Radiation efficiency' of flames. A number of workers have measured the heat radiated from flames and expressed it as a percentage of the potential heat value of the gas or other fuel burned. This is a comparatively simple experiment as it is not necessary to know the temperature, thickness, shape, or surface area of the flame. For luminous flames of coal-gas in non-aerated burners or with very low air-gas ratio, radiation efficiencies from about 16 to 18 per cent. have been found, increasing with increase of burner diameter. With theoretical air the corresponding values are about 10 to 15 per cent.

At the Imperial College [15] it was found that, for given burner diameter, as the gas consumption was increased, the radiant efficiency of luminous gas flames remained nearly steady up to a certain critical point, corresponding to the onset of turbulence in the flame, at which it suddenly fell slightly, remaining constant at the new value with further increase of gas consumption. The results are given below in Table II. For the smallest burner turbulence was not reached. For the largest burner the flame flickered at the minimum gas consumption, namely, 30 ft.^{3}/hr., and no change in the radiant efficiency was observed up to 85 ft.^{3}/hr.

TABLE II. *Radiation from Luminous Coal-gas Flames*

Burner diameter (in.)	Gas consumption (ft.^{3}/hr.)	Radiation as % of potential heat of gas burned	
		Non-turbulent	Turbulent
0·035	3·9	11·8	..
0·062	3·0– 9·5	16·6	10·0
0·125	2·5–21·0	17·6	14·6
0·266	3·0–64·0	18·2	17·2
0·47	30·0–85·0	..	18·2

Measurements were also made of the radiation from large, roughly plane, petrol flames, about 1 ft. thick, burning 4 to 8 gal. of petrol per ft. length of burner per hr. For both non-luminous and luminous flames the percentage radiation increased slightly as the rate of consumption increased, from 18 to 22 per cent. for non-luminous and from 31 to 34 per cent. for luminous flames.

For non-luminous flames the radiation should of course agree with that given by Figs. 3 and 4, but the size, shape, temperature, and composition of flame are usually known only very approximately.

BIBLIOGRAPHY

RADIATION

1. SCHMIDT, E., and ECKERT, E. 'Über die Richtungsverteilung der Wärmestrahlung von Oberflächen.' *Forsch. auf dem Gebiete des Ingenieurwes.* 1935, **6**, 175–83.

2. DAVISSON, C., and WEEKS, J. R. 'The Relation between the Total Thermal Emissive Power of a Metal and its Electrical Resistivity.' *Journal Optical Soc. Amer.* 1924 (May), **8**, No. 5, 581–605.

3. SAUNDERS, O. A. 'Notes on Some Radiation Heat Transfer Formulae.' *Proc. Phys. Soc.* 1929, **41**, 569.

4. MACKEY, C. O. *Radiant Heating and Cooling.* Bull. No. 32, Cornell University Eng. Expt. Station, 1943. See also McAdams, *Heat Transmission* (McGraw-Hill, 1942), 55.

5. HOTTEL, H. C., and EGBERT, R. B. 'Radiant Heat Transmission from Water Vapour.' *Trans. Am. Inst. Chem. Eng.* 1942, **38**, 531.

6. ULLRICH, W. Mass. Thesis in *Chem. Eng.* 1935. See W. H. McAdams, *Heat Transmission* (McGraw-Hill, 1942), 72.

7. PORT, F. J. Mass. Thesis in *Chem. Eng.* 1940. See McAdams, *Heat Transmission* (McGraw-Hill, 1942), 72.

8. WOHLENBERG, W. J., and MORROW, E. G. 'Radiation in the Pulverised Fuel Furnace.' *Trans. Am. Soc. Mech. Eng.* 1925, **47**, 127.

9. HASLAM, R. T., and HOTTEL, H. C. 'Combustion and Heat Transfer.' *Trans. Am. Soc. Mech. Eng.* 1928, **50**, FSP 9.

10. LINDMARK, T., and KIGNELL, E. 'Study on Heat Transmission in Boiler Furnaces.' *Ing. Vetenskaps Akad. Handl.* 1929, No. 91; 'Thermal Radiation in Water-cooled Boiler Furnaces.' *Ing. Vetenskaps Akad. Handl.* 1931, No. 109.

11. SHERMAN, R. A. 'Burning Characteristics of Pulverised Coal and the Radiation from their Flames.' *Trans. Am. Soc. Mech. Eng.* 1934, **56**, 401.

12. HASLAM, R. T., and BOYER, M. W. 'Radiation from Luminous Flames.' *Ind. Eng. Chem.* 1927, **19**, 4.

13. LENT, H. *Warme*, 1926, **49**, 145.

14. SHERMAN, R. A. 'Radiation from Luminous and Non-luminous Natural Gas Flames.' *Trans. Am. Soc. Mech. Eng.* 1934, **56**, 177.

15. DE MALHERBE, M. C. Ph.D. Thesis, 1946, Imperial College of Science and Technology, London.

THERMAL CONDUCTION

THERMAL conduction is a process by which heat is transmitted through solids, liquids, or gases, from the hotter to the cooler parts, the molecules with greater energy communicating some of it to neighbouring molecules with less energy. Unlike radiation by which heat can be transmitted across a vacuum, conduction can take place only through continuous matter. It is the only means by which heat can be transferred through opaque solids. In liquids or gases conduction is usually modified by fluid motion and the heat transfer is then known as convection, which is dealt with in later chapters.

Definition of thermal conductivity. The rate of heat flow, $dQ/d\tau$, by conduction across a surface of small area dS is, by the definition of thermal conductivity, k, of the medium, given by $-k\,dS(dt/dx)$, where dt/dx denotes the temperature gradient in the direction x normal to the surface. The negative sign shows that the direction of heat flow is that of decreasing temperature. Applying the law to steady heat flow across a unit cube when two opposite faces are maintained at temperatures differing by one degree, the other faces being impervious to heat, the rate of heat flow equals k, and this is an alternative way of defining k.

Considering the general case of heat conduction in a cube of small sides dx, dy, dz, the net rate of gain of heat by conduction into the cube is easily shown to be

$$k\left(\frac{\partial^2 t}{\partial x^2}+\frac{\partial^2 t}{\partial y^2}+\frac{\partial^2 t}{\partial z^2}\right)\times dxdydz,$$

and equating this to the rate of rise of heat content with time, $c\rho\,\dfrac{\partial t}{\partial \tau}dxdydz$, the differential equation of conduction

$$\frac{\partial^2 t}{\partial x^2}+\frac{\partial^2 t}{\partial y^2}+\frac{\partial^2 t}{\partial z^2}=\frac{c\rho}{k}\frac{\partial t}{\partial \tau} \tag{25}$$

is obtained. For steady flow $\partial t/\partial \tau = 0$ and t satisfies Laplace's equation, as does the potential in an electrostatic field or in a field of electric current flow through a conducting medium. It follows that, for similar boundary conditions, the shapes of isothermal surfaces and lines of heat flow in thermal conduction are identical with the shapes of equipotential surfaces and lines of electrostatic flux in electrostatics, and also with the equipotential surfaces and lines of electric current flow in the conduction of electricity. This analogy may be put to practical use (see p. 43).

Units and dimensions of thermal conductivity. From the above definition it follows that the dimensions of k are

$$\frac{Q/(\tau S)}{t/l} = Q/l\tau t,$$

Q denoting heat, τ time, and t temperature.

In the British system, k is the heat transfer in B.Th.U. per square foot per hour per degree Fahrenheit temperature difference through one foot thickness, and has dimensions B.Th.U./ft. hr. °F.

Since in conduction the heat is transferred between molecules, k is lowest for gases, for which the molecules are most widely spaced. The range of variation is very wide. For gases at extremely low pressure k is almost zero. For a natural copper crystal at $-422°$ F. a value of 7,000 B.Th.U./ft. hr. °F. has been measured.

Thermal conductivity of metals. Metals are outstandingly good thermal conductors; since they are also good electrical conductors, it is natural to suspect some relationship between thermal conductivity, k, and electrical conductivity, j. Thus k for silver or copper is of the order of 200 B.Th.U./ft. hr. °F., whereas for bismuth, which is a very poor electrical conductor, it is only about 5 B.Th.U./ft. hr. °F. Indeed, for most metals at ordinary temperatures, k/jT is constant (known as Lorenz's constant), but this ceases to apply at temperatures below $-150°$ F.

The thermal conductivity of an alloy cannot be calculated by simple proportion from the thermal conductivities of its con-constituents. Take bronze, for example, for which k is about 24, while for its constituents, 90 per cent. copper and 10 per cent. tin, k is 200 and 37 B.Th.U./ft. hr. °F. respectively. Moreover, alloying a very small proportion of one metal with another may greatly reduce its thermal conductivity. Thus commercial copper does not conduct heat anything like so well as pure copper.

For pure metals k decreases with increasing temperature, while for alloys it tends to increase.

Thermal conductivity of non-metallic solids. For non-metallic solids k is as a rule much less than for metals, but it varies over a wide range; thus, for ebonite, rubber, paraffin wax, dry wood, etc., it is of the order of 0·1, for graphite about 70 B.Th.U./ft. hr. °F.

Many solid insulating materials, such as wool, hair, down, granulated cork, asbestos wool, glass wool, etc., owe their low thermal conductivity to porosity. For, since air is a very poor conductor of heat, the air pockets formed by the pores may greatly reduce the conductivity of the material as a whole, although of course heat is transferred across them by radiation and, if they are big enough, by convection, as well as by conduction. For such materials k as a rule depends a good deal on the pressure or density of packing. There is usually an optimum density of packing which gives a minimum value of k. With looser packing than this the air spaces are too big to give the best effect since they do not check convection. With tighter packing the reduction in volume of the air spaces causes an increase in k. Many porous or fibrous materials have thermal conductivities of 0·01 to 0·03 B.Th.U./ft. hr. °F.

The thermal conductivity of non-metallic solids may either increase or decrease with temperature. For porous or fibrous materials it increases with increasing temperature, since both the conductivity of air and the radiation per degree temperature difference across the air pockets also increase with the absolute temperature. For homogeneous solids k in general decreases with increasing temperature. For crystals k is inversely proportional to the absolute temperature.

Thermal conductivity of liquids. Water has the highest thermal conductivity of non-metallic liquids, rising from about 0·33 to 0·39 B.Th.U./ft. hr. °F. as the temperature rises from

32° F. to 212° F. For most organic liquids k at ordinary temperatures is about 0·1. For ordinary oils it varies from about 0·07 to 0·10. For most liquids k seems to decrease slightly with increase of temperature, but comparatively few reliable measurements have been made.

Thermal conductivity of gases. It is difficult to measure

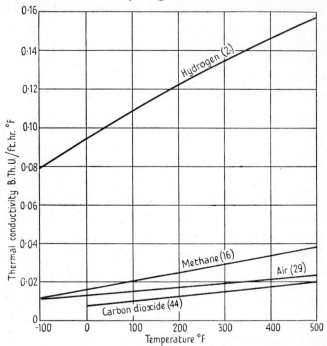

Fig. 9. Variation of thermal conductivity of gases with molecular weight and temperature.

the conductivity of a gas because of the necessity for suppressing convection currents. Methods have been devised, however, in which by working at very low pressures, or by using a thin film of gas heated from the top, convection has been reduced to negligible proportions.

It is known that, for gases, $c\mu/k$ is constant, and use can be made of this fact to deduce the values of k for different temperatures from the measured values, usually at 32° F. It will be seen from Fig. 9 that k increases with increasing temperature and tends to decrease with increasing molecular weight. Values for a wider range of temperature, derived from the somewhat more complicated Eucken's formula, are given in Table XVIII for air, carbon dioxide, hydrogen, and water vapour.

Theoretically the thermal conductivity of a gas should be independent of its pressure or density, except when extremely low, but there is some evidence of an actual slight increase with pressure. Below about one-tenth of an atmosphere or less, k decreases in nearly direct proportion to the decrease of pressure. The critical pressure at which k begins to decrease is reached when the length of the mean free path of the molecules, which increases as the density is decreased, becomes comparable with the linear size of the enclosure.

Steady and unsteady conduction. The flow of heat in a conducting body is said to be steady when the temperature at all points in the body remains constant with time, while heat is steadily transferred from the hotter to the cooler parts.

The flow is said to be unsteady when the temperature at any point changes with time, either periodically, as in a wall exposed on the outside to night and day conditions, or continuously, as in the warming-up process which always precedes the steady state.

STEADY CONDUCTION

Conduction through plane slab. Consider a flat homogeneous slab of thickness d and thermal conductivity k. Let opposite faces of the slab be maintained at temperatures t_1 and t_2 as in the diagram.

By the definition of k,

$$H = -k(dt/dx).$$

Since H must be the same for all sections parallel to the faces of the slab, if k is assumed constant dt/dx must be constant, i.e. the temperature gradient is a straight line, with slope $-H/k$, and

$$H = (k/d)(t_1-t_2) \text{ B.Th.U./ft.}^2 \text{ hr.} \tag{26}$$

Isothermals are planes parallel to the faces of the slab, and lines of heat flow are perpendicular to the isothermals.

Conduction through two plane slabs in series.

A common practical case of conduction is that through a wall composed of

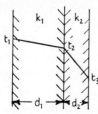

two or more layers of material of different conductivity, such, for example, as a metal wall lagged with insulating material.

Consider first two layers, of conductivity k_1 and k_2 and thickness d_1 and d_2, as in the diagram. If t_1 and t_3 are the temperatures of the outer surfaces, and t_2 the temperature of the interface, then, by (26),

$$H = (k_1/d_1)(t_1-t_2) = (k_2/d_2)(t_2-t_3)$$

or $\quad Hd_1/k_1 = t_1-t_2 \quad$ and $\quad Hd_2/k_2 = t_2-t_3.$

By addition, $\quad H[(d_1/k_1)+(d_2/k_2)] = t_1-t_3$

and

$$H = \frac{1}{(d_1/k_1)+(d_2/k_2)} (t_1-t_3). \tag{27}$$

Surface heat transfer coefficient.

The heat transfer H per unit area per unit time, between a surface and its surroundings, may be expressed in terms of a surface heat transfer coefficient $\alpha = H/\theta$. If θ, the temperature difference between surface and surroundings, is in degrees F. the units of α will be B.Th.U./ft.^{2} hr. °F.

Heat transfer between two fluids separated by a composite wall.

The result obtained above may be extended to

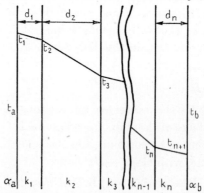

include any number n of layers in series, and also the heat transfer coefficients at the boundary wall surfaces. If $t_1, t_2,..., t_{n+1}$

are the surface temperatures of the successive layers of the wall, t_a and t_b the temperatures of the inner and outer surroundings, and α_a and α_b the inner and outer surface coefficients of heat transfer, then $H/\alpha_a = t_a-t_1$ and $H/\alpha_b = t_{n+1}-t_b$.

It follows that

$$H\left(\frac{1}{\alpha_a}+\frac{d_1}{k_1}+\frac{d_2}{k_2}+\frac{d_3}{k_3}+\ldots+\frac{d_n}{k_n}+\frac{1}{\alpha_b}\right) = t_a-t_b \quad \text{or} \quad H = U(t_a-t_b),$$

where
$$\frac{1}{U} = \frac{1}{\alpha_a}+\frac{d_1}{k_1}+\frac{d_2}{k_2}+\frac{d_3}{k_3}+\ldots+\frac{d_n}{k_n}+\frac{1}{\alpha_b}. \tag{28}$$

U is called the overall heat transfer coefficient.

It is sometimes convenient to refer to $1/\alpha_a$, d_1/k_1, etc., as resistances to heat flow; $1/U$ is the overall resistance and is equal to the sum of the separate resistances.

Conduction through a single cylindrical wall. When heat flows radially through a cylindrical wall, the heat-flow area at any radius is proportional to the radius, and therefore the temperature gradient is inversely proportional to the radius (see diagram).

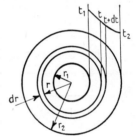

Let r_1 and r_2, t_1 and t_2 be the radii and temperatures of the inner and outer cylinder wall surfaces respectively. Consider the radial flow of heat through a thin cylindrical element of inner and outer radii and temperatures r and $r+dr$, t and $t+dt$ respectively. It is convenient to express the heat flow H_l in terms of unit length of cylinder; then

$$H_l = -k2\pi r(dt/dr) \text{ B.Th.U./ft. length hr.},$$

and since H_l is the same for all radii, we can write

$$H_l\int_{r_1}^{r_2}\frac{dr}{r} = -2\pi k\int_{t_1}^{t_2}dt,$$

whence
$$H_l = \frac{2\pi k(t_1-t_2)}{\log_e(r_2/r_1)} \text{ B.Th.U./ft. length hr.} \tag{29}$$

It follows from (29) that for given values of k and (t_1-t_2) the rate of heat flow per unit length through a cylindrical wall, depends only upon the ratio r_2/r_1. Alternatively the heat flow H per unit area of cylinder at any radius r is

$$H = \frac{H_l}{2\pi r} = \frac{k(t_1-t_2)}{r\log_e(r_2/r_1)} \text{ B.Th.U./ft.}^2 \text{ hr.,} \qquad (30)$$

H is usually calculated in terms of unit area of the inside or outside wall surface, i.e. $r = r_1$, or $r = r_2$.

The heat flow through a cylindrical wall may be found approximately by considering the wall as a flat slab of area equal to the arithmetic mean of the cylinder wall surface area, and thickness equal to the wall thickness. For very small values of r_2/r_1, the error involved in making this approximation is negligible, and even when $r_2/r_1 = 2$, the error is only 4 per cent.

Heat transfer between one fluid inside and another outside a composite cylindrical wall. Consider a composite cylindrical wall consisting of n layers; let k_1, k_2,..., k_n be the conductivities, r_1, r_2,..., r_{n+1} the radii, t_a and t_b the temperatures of the surroundings on the inner and outer sides of the wall, and α_a and α_b the inner and outer surface heat transfer coefficients. It can be shown that

$$H_l = \frac{2\pi(t_b-t_a)}{\dfrac{1}{r_1\alpha_a}+\dfrac{\log_e(r_2/r_1)}{k_1}+\dfrac{\log_e(r_3/r_2)}{k_2}+\cdots+\dfrac{\log_e(r_{n+1}/r_n)}{k_n}+\dfrac{1}{r_{n+1}\alpha_b}}$$

$$\text{B.Th.U./ft. length hr.} \quad (31)$$

Steady conduction through bodies of complex shape. Mathematical analyses of heat conduction for a number of cases have been obtained, e.g. rectangular blocks, square plates, etc., and for these the reader is referred to text-books on this subject [1, 2].

In all but the simplest geometrical cases, formal mathematical solution becomes very complex, or quite intractable, and other methods must be employed.

The approximate methods of Langmuir, Adams, and Meikle (an account of which is given in the *Dictionary of Applied Physics*, vol. i, p. 463) are of practical interest, since they show

how to calculate the contribution of the edges and corners to the heat loss from a rectangular bar, a rectangular box, or a thin rectangular plate, covered on all sides by a layer of insulating material of uniform thickness.

A graphical method of sketching isothermals and lines of flow, from which heat flow can be deduced, for two-dimensional flow in a solid of any shape, with given boundary conditions, has been described by Awbery and Schofield [3].

The relaxation methods developed by Southwell [4] may be used to plot a two-dimensional temperature field to any desired degree of accuracy. The method is a numerical one, in which the field is divided into a mesh or network. The first step in the solution is to guess the temperature at each junction in the network; these temperatures are then adjusted, step by step, by the relaxation procedure, until the correct final solution is approached.

Electrical analogies [3]. The laws of conduction of heat and electricity are essentially similar, lines of heat flow and isothermals corresponding to lines of electrical current flow and equipotentials. This analogy can conveniently be made use of to find the heat flow and temperatures in bodies of awkward shape. For example, if a model is constructed in which the isothermal boundaries are replaced by metallic surfaces, and the heat insulating medium by an electrolyte, and potential difference is applied between the boundaries, the equipotentials, which can be found experimentally, coincide with the isothermals in the corresponding heat-flow problem.

The total heat flow is proportional to the reciprocal of the electrical resistance of the electrolytic model. Thus if a second model is made of a simple shape for which the heat flow can be calculated, the heat flow in the complicated shape can be deduced from the relative values of the electrolytic resistances of the two models.

An alternative method suitable for problems of two-dimensional heat flow is to make the model of metal foil and to measure the resistance of the foil between two thick metal electrodes arranged in the form of the isothermal surfaces.

EXAMPLE 1

A rectangular tank containing water at 150° F. loses 200 B.Th.U./ft.² hr. to its surroundings. When it is insulated with 2-in. material of $k = 0.1$ B.Th.U./ft. hr. °F. the outer surface of the insulation takes up a temperature of 80° F. Find the reduction in the heat loss.

Solution. The rate of heat transfer through the insulation will be
$$(k/d)(150-80) = \frac{0.1}{2/12} \times 70 = 42 \text{ B.Th.U./ft.}^2 \text{ hr.}$$

The reduction is therefore $(200-42)$ on 200, i.e. 79 per cent.

EXAMPLE 2

A furnace wall consists of firebrick 6 in. thick for which $k = 0.8$. In the steady state the furnace side of the wall is at 1,000° F. and the outer side 350° F. When 1 in. of a magnesia insulation of $k = 0.05$ is added, its outer surface takes up a temperature of 200° F. Assuming the furnace side of the wall to remain at 1,000° F., what reduction in the heat loss is brought about by the addition of the magnesia, and what is the temperature at the interface of brick and magnesia?

Solution. The original heat loss is given by
$$\frac{0.8}{1/2}(1000-350) = 1040 \text{ B.Th.U./ft.}^2 \text{ hr.}$$

With the magnesia, the temperature t at the interface is given by
$$\frac{0.8}{1/2}(1000-t) = \frac{0.05}{1/12}(t-200), \text{ whence } t = 782° \text{ F.}$$

and
$$H = \frac{0.8}{1/2}(1000-782) = 349 \text{ B.Th.U./ft.}^2 \text{ hr.,}$$

or
$$\frac{0.05}{1/12}(782-200) = 349 \text{ B.Th.U./ft.}^2 \text{ hr.}$$

The reduction in H is thus $(1040-349)$ on 1040, i.e. 66 per cent.

EXAMPLE 3

A steam pipe of outer diameter 1 in. is covered with two layers of insulation each 1 in. thick, the conductivity of one being five times that of the other. Prove that the insulation is about

13 per cent. more efficacious when the better insulating material is put on the inside than when it is put on the outside.

Solution. The conduction through unit length of a pipe of inner and outer radii r_1 and r_2 is from (29) $2\pi k\theta/\log_e(r_2/r_1.)$

The resistance to heat flow in the above problem with the better insulating material (*a*) on the inside and (*b*) on the outside is therefore:

(*a*) $$\frac{\log_e 3}{2\pi k} + \frac{\log_e(5/3)}{2\pi \times 3k},$$

(*b*) $$\frac{\log_e 3}{2\pi \times 3k} + \frac{\log_e(5/3)}{2\pi k}.$$

Since it is only the ratio of these which is required, 2π and k can be cancelled out and logs taken to the base 10, giving relative resistances:

(*a*) $$\frac{\log 3}{1} + \frac{\log 1\cdot67}{3} = 0\cdot477 + \frac{0\cdot223}{3} = 0\cdot55,$$

(*b*) $$\frac{\log 3}{3} + \frac{\log 1\cdot67}{1} = \frac{0\cdot477}{3} + 0\cdot223 = 0\cdot48.$$

The apparent conductivity of the double layer in case (*a*) is thus seen to be less than that in case (*b*) by $100(0\cdot55-0\cdot48)/0\cdot55$ per cent. = 13 per cent.

Unsteady Conduction

Since in unsteady conduction the temperature at any point in a body changes with time, it follows that heat is absorbed (or given up) by the body, and therefore its heat capacity, as well as its conductivity, is involved in calculations; in this case the heat flow, given by expression (25), depends upon the ratio $k/c\rho$, which is called the thermal diffusivity, c being the specific heat per unit mass and ρ the density.

Unsteady heat-flow calculations arise in connexion with a wide variety of industrial processes. In some cases it is required to find the temperature distribution throughout a body at any instant of time, to determine, for example, the temperature stresses set up in a hot mass of steel when it is quenched in a cold fluid. In other cases the temperature variation with time at any point in a body may be required, for example, in food processing, manufacture of ceramics, etc., where it is required to bring the interior of a body to a given temperature and to maintain it for a suitable time. In gases heat is transferred to or from the surface of the body by convection or radiation or both.

A case of unsteady conduction often met with is that of a solid at a uniform initial temperature t_0, suddenly exposed to

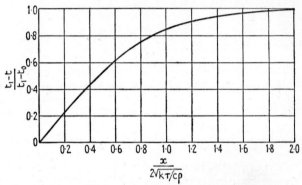

Fig. 10. Temperature variation with distance, and time, in an infinitely thick slab whose surface temperature is suddenly changed.

surroundings at a uniform constant temperature t_1. It is convenient to arrange the variables involved in four dimensionless groups, namely,

$$\frac{t_1-t}{t_1-t_0}, \quad \frac{\alpha l}{k}, \quad \left(\frac{k}{c\rho}\right)\frac{\tau}{l^2}, \quad \text{and} \quad \frac{x}{l},$$

where t is the temperature, at time τ, at a point at distance x from some reference point, α is the surface heat transfer coefficient, assumed constant, and l is a characteristic linear dimension of the body. Mathematical solutions for a number of geometrically simple cases have been derived and plotted in the form of charts in terms of these groups. A simple case which does not involve the surface heat transfer coefficient is that of an infinitely thick slab, initially at a uniform temperature t_0, whose surface is suddenly altered to and kept at a different temperature t_1, for which the temperature distribution can be obtained from Fig. 10, in which $(t_1-t)/(t_1-t_0)$ is plotted against $x/2\sqrt{(k\tau/c\rho)}$, where x is the distance from the surface. This can be applied without much error to a finite slab, until the temperature of the second surface has altered appreciably. After this stage the heat transfer between the second surface and its surroundings has to be taken into account. Similarly, from Fig. 11, in which

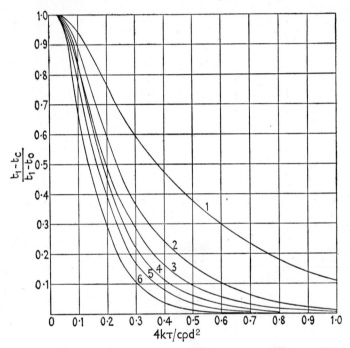

Fig. 11. Temperature, t_c, at the centre of bodies of various shapes, initially at a uniform temperature, t_0, at time, τ, after the surfaces have been suddenly altered to, and maintained at, temperature, t_1.

(1) Slab: d = thickness; (2) Square bar: d = side; (3) Long cylinder: d = diameter; (4) Cube: d = side; (5) Cylinder, length = diameter: d = diameter; (6) Sphere: d = diameter.

$(t_1-t_c)/(t_1-t_0)$ is plotted against $4k\tau/c\rho d^2$, the temperature, t_c, at the mid-plane, axis, or centre of bodies of various shapes, when the surfaces, originally at t_0, are suddenly altered to and maintained at t_1, can be obtained.

Other cases have been dealt with by Gurney and Lurie [5], Hottel [6], Newman [7], Schack [8], etc. Figs. 12 and 13 are Schack's charts for a slab of finite thickness d, but infinite extent, heated on both sides, l being taken as $d/2$. Fig. 12 gives

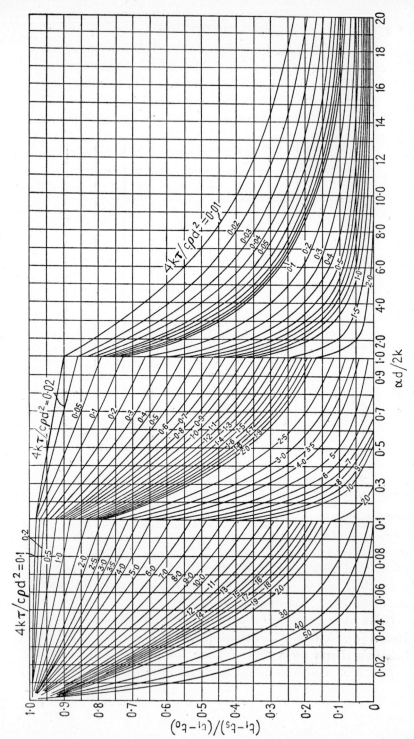

Fig. 12. Surface temp. t_s of a slab, initially at a uniform temp. t_0, and suddenly exposed on both sides to surroundings at a different temp. t_1.

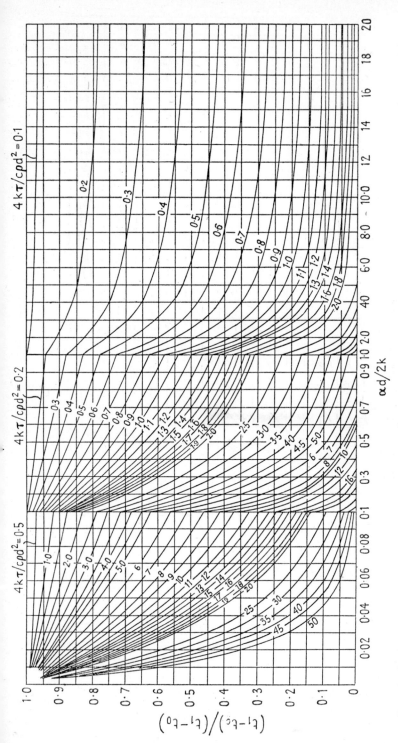

Fig. 13. Centre plane temperature t_c of a slab, initially at a uniform temperature t_0, and suddenly exposed on both sides to surroundings at a different temperature t_1.

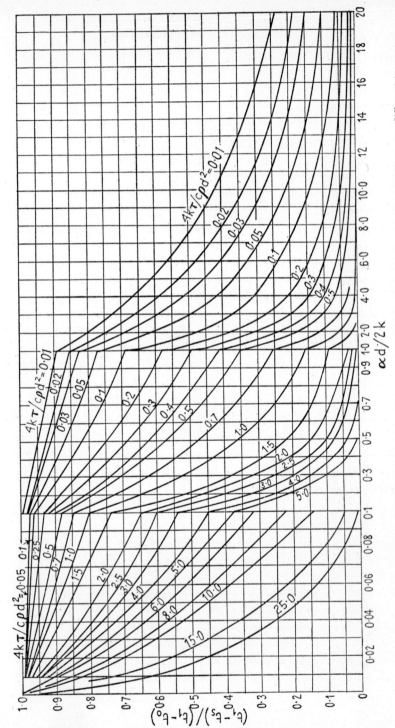

Fig. 14. Surface temp. t_s of a long cylinder, initially at a uniform temp. t_0, and suddenly exposed to surroundings at a different temp. t_1.

curves of $(t_1-t_s)/(t_1-t_0)$ against $\alpha d/2k$, for various values of $\dfrac{k}{c\rho}\dfrac{4\tau}{d^2}$ for finding the surface temperature, t_s, after different times. Fig. 13 gives similar curves of $(t_1-t_c)/(t_1-t_0)$ for finding the mid-plane temperatures, t_c, after different times. The ratio x/l is a constant for each set of curves and is therefore not involved.

Figs. 14 and 15 are the corresponding curves for an infinitely long cylinder, of diameter d.

Since the charts are non-dimensional, any consistent system of units may be employed.

The value of such charts has been widened by Newman, who has shown that they can also be used for two- or three-dimensional problems. Consider, for example, an infinitely long rectangular bar heated on all sides, with sides of length a and b in the direction of x and y axes respectively (Fig. 16). Put $(t_1-t)/(t_1-t_0) = Y$, where t is the temperature at any instant at any point (x, y) in the cross-section; then it can be shown that $Y = Y_a Y_b$, where Y_a is the dimensionless temperature ratio at the same instant for a plane at distance x from one face of a slab of thickness a, heated on both sides. Thus from Figs. 12 and 13 the value of Y may be found at the axis, the edge, and the centre of each side, as shown in Fig. 17.

Similarly, for a rectangular solid $a \times b \times c$, Y at any point is given by $Y_a \times Y_b \times Y_c$ for that point, and may be found at each corner, the mid-point of each edge, the centre of each face, and the centre of the body.

If Y_r gives the temperature in an infinitely long cylinder, then Y for a finite cylinder of length l is given by $Y_r Y_l$ and may be found for points on the circumference, and at the centre of each end, and for points on the circumference, and at the centre of the mid-plane.

General problem of unsteady conduction. The method outlined in the previous section, in which prepared charts are employed, is obviously limited to the particular shapes covered by the charts, and to the relatively simple cases in which the surface heat transfer coefficient and the diffusivity of the material remain constant.

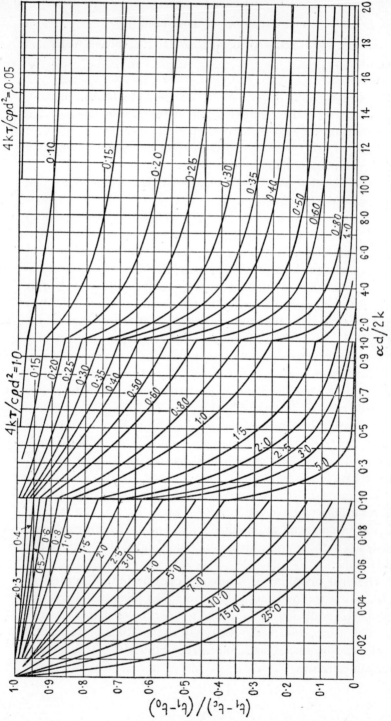

FIG. 15. Temperature t_c along the axis of a long cylinder, initially at a uniform temperature t_0, and suddenly exposed to surroundings at a different temperature t_1.

In practical problems things are not usually of simple geometric form, and t_1 and $k/c\rho$ may vary. Formal mathematical solution then becomes intractable, and approximate solutions are resorted to. These are of two principal types, namely, numerical and analogical. Electric [9] and hydraulic [10]

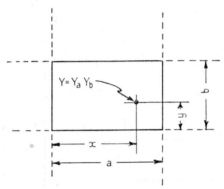

$Y = Y_a \, Y_b$

FIG. 16. Temperature at any point in a long rectangular bar, heated on all sides.

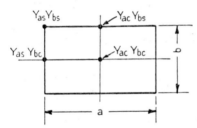

$Y_{as} Y_{bs}$ $Y_{ac} Y_{bs}$

$Y_{as} Y_{bc}$ $Y_{ac} Y_{bc}$

FIG. 17. Temperatures in a long rectangular bar, heated on all sides, which may be found from Figs. 12 and 13.

analogies have been described in the literature. In all the numerical methods the conducting body is divided into a network in small but finite steps, in one, two, or three dimensions, and the temperature distribution at some instant is assumed to be known; then the temperature distribution after a small but finite interval of time is found by equating the heat flow by conduction into each element of the network to the heat gained by that element. The space and time intervals may be chosen independently or may be related in such a way as to simplify the calculation. A well-known method of the latter type for one-dimensional flow, which is usually applied graphically, is described below.

Graphical method of plotting temperature distribution curves in one-dimensional unsteady conduction. Suppose, for instance, given the initial temperature distribution through the thickness of a large plane slab, the subsequent temperature

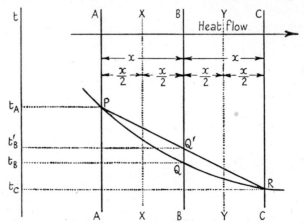

FIG. 18. Graphical method for unsteady conduction.

distribution at any given time is required; the slab is divided up into a number of imaginary layers each of thickness x, by planes AA, BB, CC, etc., as in Fig. 18. Let PQR be the temperature distribution at any instant, t_A, t_B, t_C, etc., being the temperatures at AA, BB, CC, etc. Let XX, YY, etc., be the mid-planes of the layers. Consider the rate at which heat is flowing into the layer between XX and YY. The temperature gradient at XX is, to a first approximation, equal to the slope of PQ; i.e. to $(t_A - t_B)/x$. Hence the rate of heat flow per unit area across XX is approximately $\dfrac{k(t_A - t_B)}{x}$. Similarly the rate of heat flow across YY is $\dfrac{k(t_B - t_C)}{x}$, and the net rate at which the layer is gaining heat is thus $\dfrac{k(t_A + t_C - 2t_B)}{x}$. Since the volume of the layer per unit surface area is x, the rate at which its temperature increases is $\dfrac{k(t_A+t_C-2t_B)}{\rho c x^2}$, and the temperature rise in

time τ is $\dfrac{k\tau(t_A+t_C-2t_B)}{\rho c x^2}$. By choosing a time increment τ, equal

to $\rho c x^2/2k$, the temperature rise is $\dfrac{t_A+t_C}{2}-t_B$, and the new

temperature t_B' is $(t_A+t_C)/2$, represented by Q', the intersection
of a straight line PR, with BB. The new temperatures t_A' and
t_C' can be obtained in a similar manner.

EXAMPLE

A steel slab, 1 in. thick, initially at 50° F. throughout, is
perfectly insulated on one face; the other face is suddenly

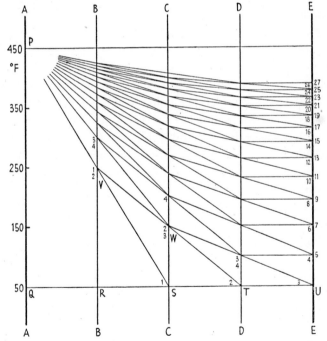

increased to and maintained at 450° F. Plot a curve showing
the temperature variation, with time, of the insulated face,
taking $\rho = 480$ lb./ft.^{3}, $k = 26$ B.Th.U./ft. hr. °F., $c = 0{\cdot}13$
B.Th.U./lb. °F., irrespective of temperature.

Solution. Draw the slab as in the diagram, to a convenient scale, EE being the insulated face, AA the opposite face. Draw BB, CC, DD, dividing the slab into four equal layers, making $x = 1/48$ ft.

$$\tau = \frac{\rho c x^2}{2k} = \frac{480 \times 0 \cdot 13}{2 \times 26 \times 48 \times 48} \text{ hr.} = 1 \cdot 875 \text{ sec.}$$

Choosing a suitable scale, draw the initial temperature distribution $PQRSTU$. Then, as shown in the previous section, the temperature at BB after time τ is given by V, the intersection of PS, with BB, and the temperature at CC is given by S, the intersection of RT with CC, i.e. the temperature at CC is as yet unchanged. The new temperature distribution is therefore $PVSTU$. After a further time τ, the temperature distribution will be $PVWTU$, and so on. It is convenient to regard the slab as one-half of a slab 2 in. thick, heated on both sides, in which there is no heat flow across the mid-plane; thus the graphical construction in the layer $DDEE$ is done by visualizing a mirror image of this layer on the opposite side of EE.

The numerals at points on the diagram represent time in units of τ (1·875 sec.) to which the points correspond; it will be seen that the construction gives the same temperature at any point, for pairs of successive time intervals, this temperature actually corresponding to an intermediate time interval. This often occurs when using this method, and then necessitates drawing smoothed curves of either temperature against distance for any instant, or temperature against time for any point. In this example a smoothed curve of temperature against time is drawn for the insulated face EE in the accompanying diagram, exact values being shown for comparison.

The number of layers into which the body is divided must always be chosen to suit the requirements of the problem. In this case a reasonably accurate solution has been obtained by using only four layers, and there would be no sense in using more. If, however, the temperature variation near the surface during the early stages of heating were required, a smaller value of x would have to be chosen. It is sometimes convenient to use a small value of x for the early stages of heating, changing to a larger value for the later stages.

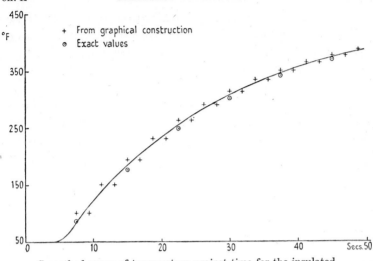

Smoothed curve of temperature against time for the insulated face EE.

The construction as used in the previous example can easily be extended to cases where the surface temperature varies with time in some specified manner. Usually, however, the surrounding temperature t_1 and not the surface temperature is known, and the method must then be modified so that the temperature distribution in the slab can be found from t_1 and the surface coefficient of heat transfer, α. Suppose that at any instant the surface temperature is t_s; then the rate of heat flow through unit area of the surface is given by $\alpha(t_1 - t_s)$. This must be equal to the rate at which heat is conducted into the surface of the slab,

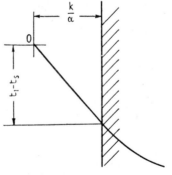

i.e. to $-k\left(\dfrac{\partial t}{\partial x}\right)_{x=0}$ so that

$$\left(\frac{\partial t}{\partial x}\right)_{x=0} = -\frac{\alpha}{k}(t_1 - t_s).$$

Hence if in the graphical construction a pole O is drawn as in the diagram at distance k/α outside the surface, and at temperature t_1, a line joining O to t_s will have a gradient $(\partial t/\partial x)_{x=0}$ and will be tangential, at the surface, to the temperature gradient in the solid. The space between O and the surface may be regarded as a layer of material of the same conductivity as the body, but having no heat capacity; the rate of heat conduction through such a layer would clearly be equal to $\alpha(t_1 - t_s)$.

The subsequent graphical procedure to be adopted when α and t_1 are given depends on whether k/α is less or greater than

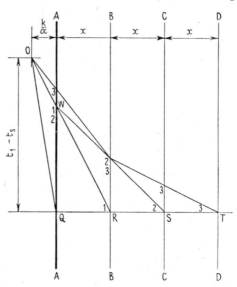

FIG. 19. Graphical method for unsteady conduction modified to include the surface coefficient α. Case when $k/\alpha < x/2$.

$x/2$. Fig. 19 shows the procedure for k/α less than $x/2$ where the body is divided as before. Suppose that $QRST$ represents the initial uniform temperature distribution in the body, then a straight line OQ would be the initial temperature gradient in the imaginary surface layer. After time $\tau = \rho c x^2/2k$, the temperature gradient would be given approximately by $OWRST$, where OWR is a straight line, with W at the surface giving the surface temperature.

When k/d is greater than $x/2$, the construction is modified as in Fig. 20, the first layer between AA and BB being $x/2$, instead of x, in thickness and a construction line XX at $x/2$, outside the surface, added. As before, suppose the initial temperature distribution to be $OQRST$, and let U be the intersection of OQ with XX. Then the temperature at BB after time $\tau = \rho c x^2 / 2k$ will be given by the intersection V of US with BB, and the new temperature distribution will be given by $OWVST$.

Subsequent temperature gradients are indicated in Figs. 19 and 20 by numerals.

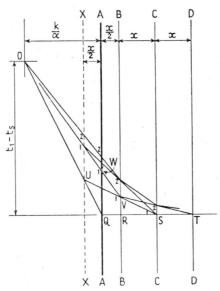

Fig. 20. Graphical method for unsteady conduction modified to include the surface coefficient α. Case when $k/\alpha > x/2$.

The graphical method has been extended to composite walls, to cylinders, to spheres, to walls exposed to surroundings subject to periodic changes of temperature, etc. Sherwood and Reed [11] have suggested a modification to the construction to allow for the variation of diffusivity with temperature.

Clearly the results of the graphical procedures described could be obtained by equivalent numerical operations, which would cut out graphical inaccuracies, but the graphical method has the advantage of providing a picture of the temperature changes taking place. Emmons [12] has given a numerical method for two-dimensional problems, in which the time and space increments are related as in the graphical method, and Dusinberre [13] a more general method for one-dimensional flow, in which the time and space increments are chosen independently, and thus greater accuracy is obtained.

EXAMPLE

A slab of material 2 in. thick, of specific heat, c, 0.4 B.Th.U./°F. lb., and density, ρ, 30 lb./ft.^{3}, is clamped between two electrically heated plates, kept at 250° F. If the initial temperature, t_0, of the slab is 60° F., and the temperature, t_c, at the midplane after 10 min., τ, is 100° F., what is its thermal conductivity?

Solution. Assuming the surface temperature, t_s, of the slab immediately becomes 250° F., $(t_1-t_c)/(t_1-t_0) = 0.79$, and, from Fig. 11, $4k\tau/c\rho d^2 = 0.18$, whence

$$k = \frac{0.18 \times 0.4 \times 30 \times 60}{4 \times 6 \times 6 \times 10} = 0.09 \text{ B.Th.U./ft. hr. °F.}$$

BIBLIOGRAPHY

CONDUCTION

1. CARSLAW, H. S., and JAEGER, J. C. *Conduction of Heat in Solids* (Clarendon Press, 1947).
2. INGERSOLL, L. R., and ZOBEL, O. J. *Mathematical Theory of Heat Conduction* (Ginn, Boston, 1913).
3. AWBERY, J. H., and SCHOFIELD, F. H. 'The Effect of Shape on the Heat Loss through Insulation.' *Proc. 5th International Congress Refrig.* 1929, **3**, 591.
4. SOUTHWELL, R. V. *Relaxation Methods in Theoretical Physics* (Clarendon Press, 1946).
5. GURNEY, H. P., and LURIE, J. 'Charts for Estimating Temperature Distributions in Heating or Cooling Solid Shapes.' *Ind. Eng. Chem.* 1923, **15**, 1170.
6. See McADAMS, W. H. *Heat Transmission* (McGraw-Hill, 1942).
7. NEWMAN, A. B. 'Heating and Cooling Rectangular and Cylindrical Solids.' *Ind. Eng. Chem.* 1936, **28**, 545.
8. SCHACK, A. 'Zur Berechnung des zeitlichen und örtlichen Temperaturverlaufs beim Glühvorgang.' *Stahl und Eisen*, 1930, **50**, 1290.
9. PASCHKIS, V., and BAKER, H. D. 'A method of determining Unsteady State Heat Transfer by means of an Electrical Analogy.' *Trans. A.S.M.E.* 1942, **64**, 105.

10. MOORE, A. D. 'A Hydrodynamic Calculating Machine for solving Unsteady State Problems in Heat Transfer.' *Ind. Eng. Chem.* 1936, **28**, 704.
11. SHERWOOD, T. K., and REED, C. E. *Applied Mathematics in Chemical Engineering* (McGraw-Hill).
12. EMMONS, H. W. 'Numerical Solution of Heat Conduction Problems.' *Trans. A.S.M.E.* 1943, **65**, 607.
13. DUSINBERRE, G. M. 'Numerical Methods for Transient Heat Flow.' *Trans. A.S.M.E.* 1945, **67**, 703.

III
DIMENSIONAL ANALYSIS OF CONVECTION

CALCULATIONS of heat transfer by convection are complicated by the large number of different variables involved. Fortunately in most applications these variables can be grouped together into relatively few 'dimensionless groups' or 'dimensionless numbers', thus reducing the number of effective variables to be dealt with experimentally. This grouping is done by dimensional analysis, which is now widely used in scientific work. Although much that has been written on the fundamentals of the method is hardly important to engineers, it is essential to understand the physical basis of the particular groupings of variables used for different problems, and the conditions in which the results are likely to hold good in practice. Some simple examples may best introduce the method.

Motion under gravity. As a very elementary example, suppose it is required to find the height h to which a mass m would rise if projected vertically with velocity v *in vacuo*. It would be expected that h would depend upon v, m, and g. Further consideration suggests that the significant quantities are the initial kinetic energy and the final gain in potential energy due to rising a height h against gravity. If the former, which is proportional to mv^2, were increased in any ratio, the latter, which is proportional to mgh, would be expected to increase in the same ratio. Hence mv^2/mgh or v^2/gh is constant, and h is proportional to v^2/g. In this simple example from mechanics, insertion of the numerical constants shows that $v^2/gh = 2$; but the method is applicable to problems where the numerical factors, or even the mathematical expressions for the quantities concerned, are not known, whether because of awkward two- or three-dimensional conditions or because the fundamental differential equations are too difficult to solve.

Viscous flow. Consider another simple problem, this time less amenable to mathematical solution. Suppose a solid to be placed in a uniform stream of viscous fluid, velocity v, density ρ, and viscosity μ, and that it is required to find the pattern of flow, or distribution of velocity, around the solid. At first sight this would be expected to depend upon v, ρ, μ, and l, where l is any linear dimension of the solid, the shape of which is assumed fixed, so that all its dimensions are known when l is known. Further consideration suggests that the essential physical process involved is the retarding of the fluid, as it flows past the solid, by the action of viscosity. The forces of viscous drag destroy a certain quantity of momentum per unit time. If, therefore, both the oncoming momentum and the viscous drag forces are altered in the same proportion, the effect should be to leave the flow pattern unchanged. Since the former is proportional to ρv^2 per unit area, and the latter to $\mu v/l$ per unit area, the ratio $\rho v l/\mu$ would be expected to determine the flow pattern. This is, of course, the well-known Reynolds number, Re.

This argument needs a little further explanation in that the words 'per unit area' are used first to denote the area across which the oncoming fluid flows and secondly the area across which the viscous shear forces act. But if the shape remains the same, these areas are always in the same ratio.

The scale effect and dimensional analysis. Since linear size is included among the variables, dimensional analysis can be used to find the effect of change in linear scale or size without change of shape or other variables. For example, in viscous flow a change of l alters Re and therefore also alters the flow pattern. But if scale change is accompanied by changes in any or all of the other variables so as to keep the Reynolds number the same, the flow pattern will not be altered. Thus, for the same oncoming velocity the streamlines round a body in air at 45° F. are identical in shape with those round a similar body one-tenth the size in water also at 45° F., since at this temperature the kinematic viscosity (μ/ρ) of the water is one-tenth that of the air.

Two systems of different size for which the physical properties at corresponding points are in the same ratio are termed 'similar' or sometimes 'dynamically similar', although the definition is not restricted to dynamics. The conditions for 'similarity' are equality of the appropriate groups or parameters and identical shape of all boundaries. For this reason the method of dimensions is sometimes called the Principle of Similarity or Principle of Similitude. The method of dimensions compares geometrically similar systems, showing how they are affected by changes of scale or of other variables. It cannot compare geometrically dissimilar systems, which would require detailed analysis of each case.

Determining the arrangement of variables in groups: Method of indices. The appropriate groups governing any problem may be found as in the examples given above, but such methods require experience and insight of the physical processes involved. A more formal solution can be found by the method of indices, an algebraic device for arranging any given set of variables in all possible combinations to form similar quantities, such as energies, forces, heat fluxes, etc. Ratios of pairs of these then form the determining groups. The method of indices is based on the idea of 'dimensions', which must first be explained.

All physical measurements are made in terms of units, which may be either fundamental or derived, according to whether they are defined independently or in terms of other simpler units. Length, mass, and time are examples of fundamental units; velocity, acceleration, and viscosity of derived units. The value of any derived unit changes when the fundamental units on which it is based are changed, and the power of a fundamental unit to which a derived unit is proportional is known as its 'dimension' in that unit. For example, acceleration has dimensions 1 in length and -2 in time, because it is directly proportional to the unit of length and inversely proportional to the square of the unit of time.

To find the dimensions of a product the dimensions of each factor must clearly be added. For example, the dimensions of (density × velocity × length) are 1 in mass, -1 in length (-3 from density, 1 from velocity, and 1 from length), and -1 in time. If any two combinations of variables represent the same kind of physical quantity they must obviously have the same total dimensions, and their ratio must be independent of fundamental units, i.e. must have zero dimensions in all such units.

For example, any combination of variables representing energy must have total dimensions 1 in mass, 2 in length, and -2 in time, and the ratio of any two energies must be dimensionless in mass, length, and time.

The problem of determining all possible arrangements of any given set of variables into dimensionless groups can be solved by assuming a general form of group with unknown indices of the variables, and solving for these unknowns by equations expressing the fact that the whole group is dimensionless in each fundamental unit.

For example, in the case of viscous flow already considered the flow pattern may be assumed to depend on a group

$$v^{x_1} l^{x_2} \rho^{x_3} \mu^{x_4},$$

where x_1, x_2, x_3, x_4 are unknown indices, at least one of which must obviously be negative. Since the dimensions of any quantity raised to a power x are x times the dimensions of the quantity itself, equating the overall dimensions to zero gives

$$\text{in length: } x_1 + x_2 - 3x_3 - x_4 = 0$$
$$\text{in mass: } x_3 + x_4 = 0$$
$$\text{in time: } -x_1 - x_4 = 0.$$

Thus are formed, in this case, three equations in four unknowns, any three of which can be found in terms of the fourth. Solving in terms of x_3 gives $x_1 = x_3$, $x_2 = x_3$, and $x_4 = -x_3$, and the general form of the dimensionless group may be written $(v\rho l/\mu)^{x_3}$. The expression inside the brackets is the dimensionless group required (Reynolds number), and all that can be deduced is that the flow pattern depends on this arrangement of variables, the values of the index x_3 and also of any constant being undetermined.

More detailed examination of the method of indices.
Before applying dimensional methods to the study of convection it may be helpful to consider in more detail the method of indices, which, being merely algebra, can only yield physical information previously fed in. In the previous example of viscous flow the information peculiar to the problem is fed in by (a) selecting the

appropriate variables v, l, ρ, and μ upon which the process is assumed to depend, and (b) selecting the units which are to be considered as fundamental in the system of units employed. Alternative assumptions in either (a) or (b) would give a different final result.

For example, if viscosity were omitted, the remaining indices would reduce to zero, showing that it is impossible to form a dimensionless group in terms of v, ρ, and l alone, and that the flow pattern is independent of these variables. Such is the case in the flow of non-viscous fluids, the pattern being determined solely by the shape of the solid boundaries.

Again, if fluid compressibility were included as a fifth variable, as would obviously be necessary if the speeds were so high that the effect of fluid pressure on density were considerable, a different result would ensue. Compressibility may conveniently be allowed for by introducing pressure, p, in addition to density, ρ. Writing the general form of the dimensionless group as

$$v^{x_1} l^{x_2} \rho^{x_3} \mu^{x_4} p^{x_5},$$

the equations expressing zero dimensions in each fundamental unit become

$$\text{in length: } x_1 + x_2 - 3x_3 - x_4 - x_5 = 0$$
$$\text{in mass: } x_3 + x_4 + x_5 = 0$$
$$\text{in time: } -x_1 - x_4 - 2x_5 = 0,$$

remembering that pressure has dimensions 1 in mass, -1 in length, and -2 in time. Solving in terms of x_4 and x_5 gives

$$x_1 = -x_4 - 2x_5$$
$$x_3 = -x_4 - x_5$$
$$x_2 = -x_4$$

and the general dimensionless group becomes

$$\left(\frac{\mu}{v\rho l}\right)^{x_4} \left(\frac{p}{\rho v^2}\right)^{x_5},$$

showing that the problem is now determined by two dimensionless groups, namely, the Reynolds number $v\rho l/\mu$ and a new number $\rho v^2/p$ which is proportional to the square of v/v_s, where v_s is the velocity of propagation of sound waves of small amplitude in the gas ($v_s = \sqrt{(\gamma p/\rho)}$, where γ is a constant). The method of indices, of course, gives no clue to the way in which these two dimensionless groups of variables affect the problem or to the numerical constants concerned. The group v/v_s is known as the Mach number; only when compressibility is known to have negligible effect can it be left out.

The selection of variables in any problem is a vital matter. The fewer the variables taken into account the smaller the resulting number of dimensionless groups and the more useful therefore the final answer. On the other hand, the omission of significant variables leads to over-simplification and to results which may not be valid.

Since each fundamental unit yields an equation for the unknown indices, the number of dimensionless groups is a minimum when the maximum number of units are regarded as fundamental. There is usually no difficulty in deciding whether a unit is fundamental or derived, but in some cases care is needed. In the viscous flow example quoted there was no doubt of velocity and density being derived units, but, to take an impossibly extreme case, if the speeds were high enough for the effects of relativity to be appreciable, mass could no longer be taken as fundamental since it would depend on velocity. A more important practical example arises in convection, where heat may legitimately be regarded as fundamental although it is in fact a form of energy. This is because convertibility between heat energy and mechanical or dynamic energy does not in general come into problems of convection as it would, for example, in problems where the heat generated by friction was significant.

Shape as a variable. Only when the shape is fixed can a system be completely described geometrically by one linear dimension. Systems of different shapes can be regarded as having varying ratios of lengths in different directions and in some cases a series of shapes may be so dealt with by dimensional analysis. For example, the convection heat transfer from circular cylinders of different lengths depends on the dimensionless group length/diameter which may be included along with the other groups.

It will be realized that in considering the flow pattern around the body the dependent variable is in fact the shape of the streamlines, etc., which is mathematically described in terms of dimensionless ratios of lengths which in this case form the dependent variable dimensionless groups.

Dimensionless groups containing dependent variables. So far the only independent variables determining a problem have been considered. If it is required to find the relation between dependent and independent variables, each dependent variable must be arranged in a dimensionless group with independent variables. For example, if interest centres on the direct forces, F, upon a body in a stream of viscous fluid, dimensional analysis shows that $F/\rho v^2$ is determined by the Reynolds number $v\rho l/\mu$. To arrive formally at the dependent variable group arrangement the method of indices is used as above, except that, instead of equating the dimensions of the general groups to zero, they are equated with those of the dependent variable, in this case F.

Alternative forms of groups. New dimensionless groups can be formed by multiplying, dividing, inverting, etc., the original groups, and may be used in their place. For example, instead of $v\rho l/\mu$ and $p/\rho v^2$ their product $pl/\mu v$ and quotient $v^3 \rho^2 l/\mu p$ could be used. It is convenient that in each group there should be one variable peculiar to that group, i.e. not contained in any of the others, so that, to consider the effect of changing this variable, only one group need be considered. Different groups are given by the method of indices by solving the simultaneous equations in terms of different indices, and, to obtain groups in which particular variables are confined each to one group, the corresponding indices must be chosen as the unknown in terms of which the remaining indices are expressed. For example, in the case of viscous flow treated above, solving in terms of x_4 and x_5 ensures that μ occurs only in the first group and p only in the second.

APPLICATION TO CONVECTION HEAT TRANSFER

Convection is the process by which heat is transferred between a surface and the fluid in which it is immersed; actually it is conduction in a fluid the parts of which are in relative motion. It is necessary to distinguish between 'natural' or 'free' convection, in which the fluid motion is caused solely by gravity forces due to differences of density between the hotter and cooler parts, and 'forced' convection, in which the fluid motion is caused by forces independent of the temperature of the fluid, such as externally imposed differences of pressure. Actually, even when the convection is forced, buoyancy forces are always induced by the temperature differences, and tend to set up natural convection currents; but in many practical cases the forced motion of the fluid is so rapid that natural convection is negligible in comparison. A warm surface exposed to the practically still air of an ordinary room loses heat by natural convection, while a common example of forced convection heat transfer is that between the walls of a tube and a fluid at a different temperature flowing through it at a high speed.

Consider the general problem of convection, including both forced and natural, and suppose the heat transfer H per unit surface area per unit time to depend on the quantities set out in Table III, which gives also the dimensions of these quantities in

TABLE III. *Dimensions of Quantities used in Heat Transfer*

| Quantity | Symbol | Dimensions in terms of | | | | |
		Length l	Mass m	Time τ	Temp. t	Heat Q
Forced velocity of fluid .	v	1	0	−1	0	0
Linear scale or size. .	l	1	0	0	0	0
Temperature difference between surface and fluid	θ	0	0	0	1	0
Viscosity of fluid . .	μ	−1	1	−1	0	0
Thermal conductivity of fluid	k	−1	0	−1	−1	1
Density of fluid . .	ρ	−3	1	0	0	0
Specific heat of fluid at constant pressure .	c	0	−1	0	−1	1
Coefficient of thermal expansion × acceleration due to gravity . .	ag	1	0	−2	−1	0

terms of the fundamental units of length l, mass m, time τ, temperature t, and heat Q. The reasons for choosing these particular variables and fundamental units will be more easily explained after the general analysis. Assuming H to be proportional to $v^{x_1}l^{x_2}\theta^{x_3}\mu^{x_4}k^{x_5}\rho^{x_6}c^{x_7}(ag)^{x_8}$, where x_1 to x_8 are unknown indices, and equating dimensions in terms of fundamental units of length, mass, time, temperature, and heat respectively, gives

in length: $x_1+x_2-x_4-x_5-3x_6+x_8 = -2$

in mass: $\qquad\qquad x_4+x_6-x_7 = 0$

in time: $\qquad -x_1-x_4-x_5-2x_8 = -1$

in temperature: $\quad x_3-x_5-x_7-x_8 = 0$

in heat: $\qquad\qquad\qquad x_5+x_7 = 1.$

Solving in terms of x_1, x_7, and x_8, these particular three being chosen so as to obtain groups each containing one only of the variables v, c, and ag, using each equation in turn starting from the last gives:

$$x_5 = 1-x_7$$
$$x_3 = 1+x_8$$
$$x_4 = -x_1+x_7-2x_8$$
$$x_6 = x_1+2x_8$$
$$x_2 = -1+x_1+3x_8.$$

Hence H is proportional to

$$\frac{k\theta}{l}\left(\frac{v\rho l}{\mu}\right)^{x_1}\left(\frac{c\mu}{k}\right)^{x_7}\left(\frac{ag\theta l^3\rho^2}{\mu^2}\right)^{x_8},$$

and since x_1, x_7, and x_8 are unknown, all that can be deduced is that $Hl/k\theta$ depends upon $v\rho l/\mu$, $c\mu/k$, and $ag\theta l^3\rho^2/\mu^2$. In any problem of convection, therefore, the heat transfer H is given by a relation between the dependent variable dimensionless group $Hl/k\theta$, known as the Nusselt number, Nu, and the three independent variable dimensionless groups $v\rho l/\mu$ the Reynolds number, Re, $c\mu/k$ the Prandtl number, Pr, and $ag\theta l^3\rho^2/\mu^2$ the Grashof number, Gr. The mathematical form of the relation and the numerical constants depend on the shapes of the surfaces bounding the convecting fluid, and cannot be found by dimensional analysis, but must be obtained either experimentally or by a complete mathematical analysis of the velocity, temperature, etc., of the fluid, which is rarely possible.

Convection in gases. The Prandtl number $c\mu/k$, which contains only specific fluid properties, is nearly the same for all gases and over a wide range of temperature. It may, therefore, usually be disregarded as a variable group when considering any problem of convection in a gas, thus reducing the independent variable groups to two, Re and Gr.

Natural convection. In cases of natural convection, the motion being entirely due to heat, the forced velocity v may be dropped out in the general analysis. The result, conveniently found by putting $x_1 = 0$, is to eliminate Re so that Nu becomes dependent upon Gr and Pr only, or for a gas, upon Gr only. Putting $v = 0$ does not, of course, mean that the fluid has no velocity, but only that the velocity is not an independent variable, since it is not controlled from outside the system; the fluid velocity at any point now becomes a dependent variable, and is given by a relation between Re as a dependent variable group, and Gr and Pr.

Forced convection. With true forced convection, the effects of buoyancy being negligible, the variable ag may be dropped out, since gravity no longer affects the problem. Putting $x_8 = 0$ in the general analysis, the Grashof number is eliminated, and Nu becomes dependent upon Re and Pr only, or, in the case of a gas, upon Re only.

Physical significance of groups. The Nusselt number, $Hl/k\theta$, represents the ratio of the actual convection heat transfer, H, per unit surface area per unit time, to $k\theta/l$, which is proportional to the heat transfer by conduction in the fluid at rest.

The Reynolds number, as already pointed out, may be regarded as the ratio of the oncoming fluid momentum per unit area per unit time, ρv^2, to the viscous drag force per unit area $\mu v/l$, against which it is balanced. It is the group which determines the flow pattern or velocity distribution, when a solid body is placed in a stream of viscous fluid.

The Prandtl number is the ratio of the kinematic viscosity, or momentum diffusivity, μ/ρ, to the thermal diffusivity $k/c\rho$. It represents the ratio of the fluid property governing the transfer of momentum by viscous effects due to a gradient of velocity, to the fluid property governing the transfer of heat by thermal diffusion due to a gradient of temperature. It is, therefore, the group which determines the relation of the temperature distribution in a fluid to the velocity distribution, or more generally the relation of heat transfer to fluid motion. Thus in forced convection the fluid motion is fixed by Re, and the superposition of a temperature difference between the boundary surface and the fluid causes a temperature distribution in the fluid which is fixed by Pr, together with original fluid motion. In general, therefore, the temperature distribution, and the heat transfer, are determined by both Re and Pr.

The Grashof number is more difficult to interpret simply. It is the ratio of the buoyancy force per unit area, $ag\theta\rho l$,† to the viscous drag force per unit area, $\mu v/l$. This gives $ag\theta\rho l^2/\mu v$ but, since the velocity v is a dependent variable and is determined by a relation between $v\rho l/\mu$ and the appropriate independent variable groups, v may be taken as proportional to $\mu/\rho l$, and $ag\theta\rho l^2/\mu v$ is thus proportional to $ag\theta\rho^2 l^3/\mu^2$ (the Grashof number) which contains independent variables only and expresses the relative effects of buoyancy forces and viscous forces.

Further explanation of selection of independent variables and fundamental units. The variables selected require some explanation, remembering that the dimensional method yields most useful results by keeping the number a minimum. Hence only the difference between the surface and fluid temperatures is included, and not each separately, thus assuming that the heat transfer is not affected by change in absolute temperature. This appears justified because absolute temperature can only affect the problem through its effect upon the values of the fluid properties, k, μ, ρ, etc., which are already included as separate variables. These properties, although often called physical constants, all vary with temperature and, since their variation is not allowed for, mean values must be taken. Nusselt [4]

---

† The buoyancy acceleration is proportional to ag and to the temperature difference θ. The buoyancy force on a volume of linear dimension l is therefore proportional to $ag\theta\rho l^3$, and the force per unit area to $ag\theta\rho l^3/l^2$, or $ag\theta\rho l$.

has shown how dimensional analysis can be extended to include the temperature variation of constants, obtaining as an extra dimensionless group the ratio of the absolute temperatures of surface and fluid. In certain applications, where the temperature difference between surface and fluid is big, Nusselt's method is useful, but for many purposes it suffices to consider the physical properties as constant, but to reckon their values at a mean temperature, usually, but not always, the arithmetic mean between the surface and fluid temperatures.

The specific heat c is taken at constant pressure, since the pressure differs in different parts of the fluid only because of variations in velocity and hydrostatic depth, and the effects of both of these are small compared with the absolute pressure.

The coefficient of thermal expansion a is associated as a product with gravity acceleration g, because the buoyancy force on a unit volume of fluid, given by the difference between the weight of fluid at the bulk fluid temperature which it displaces and its own weight, is $\rho_0 g - \rho g$. The coefficient of expansion a is defined by $\rho_0 = \rho(1 + a\theta)$ so, substituting for ρ_0, the acceleration becomes $ag\theta$. Since θ is already included as a variable, only ag need be included as a further variable. This simplification amounts to neglecting the effects of thermal expansion except in so far as it produces buoyancy forces, and neglects the effect on the flow pattern of change in volume due to temperature.†

The choice of fundamental units needs no comment, except, as already pointed out, that heat is regarded as independent and not as a form of kinetic energy, which is only justified provided heat energy and mechanical energy are not interchanged. In most industrial heat transfer this is permissible, but in extreme cases it might not be.

---

† An alternative, and perhaps better, form of the Grashof number is $\{(\rho_0 - \rho)gl^3\rho^2\}/\rho\mu^2$, since this gets over the difficulty of deciding at what temperature to take a when it varies appreciably over the range of temperature from the surface to the fluid. In subsequent pages $a\theta$ may therefore be regarded as replaceable by $(\rho_0/\rho) - 1$. For natural convection in gases a is thus equal to $1/T_0$, where T_0 is the absolute temperature of the gas.

The final test of the validity of the various assumptions is whether the dimensionless groups arrived at are consistent with experimental measurements of heat transfer.

Correlation of experimental data by dimensionless groups. Having applied dimensional analysis to find the appropriate dependent and independent variable groups, the relation between them usually requires experiment. For example, for forced convection in a gas, dimensional analysis shows $Hl/k\theta$ to depend only upon Re. By experiments measuring the heat transfer, say for different velocities, the numerical relation between Nu and Re may be found, and either plotted as a curve with Nu and Re as coordinates, or expressed mathematically. Such a curve once constructed may be used to read off the heat transfer under any given conditions within the range of Re studied. Its application is not limited to the conditions of the original experiments and it can, for example, be used for other gases of different viscosities and densities or for other sizes of body. The only condition is that Re should remain within the range for which the measurements were carried out and, of course, that the shape of the system should remain the same. Dimensionless groups thus greatly extend the usefulness of experimental results, since data for different sizes, different velocities, different temperatures, and different gases can all be brought together on a single curve. Separate curves must, however, be constructed for different geometrical arrangements. Cases of natural convection can of course be dealt with in a similar manner.

One of the main advantages of the similarity method of correlation is that, whereas the experimental data available are not usually sufficiently complete for constructing curves showing the dependence of the heat transfer upon each of the variable factors individually, there are in many cases enough data for drawing a single curve showing the relation between the two appropriate similarity groups. Once obtained, such a curve may be used to calculate the heat transfer for values of the individual variables outside the ranges covered by actual experiments, provided only that the values of the groups fall within the range of the curve. Unfortunately the values of the physical constants associated with convection, particularly thermal conductivity and viscosity, are not known accurately at extreme temperatures or extreme pressures. Moreover, for mixtures of fluids they cannot be obtained simply from a weighted mean. Such uncertainties obviously impose limits on the application of similarity methods of correlation.

Choice of units. The groups, being dimensionless, have the same numerical values whatever the system of units employed, provided only that consistency is maintained. For example, v must not be measured in ft./min. if k is expressed as B.Th.U./ ft. hr. °F. But if the same fundamental units are adhered to throughout, either C.G.S. or British or any other consistent units can be used; in view of the multiplicity of different units encountered in technical publications, this property of the similarity method often simplifies calculations.

Correlation of data for different shapes. Strictly speaking, dimensionless methods of correlation can be applied only to one shape of body at a time, and it is immaterial in which direction the linear dimension used is measured, so long as it is always measured in the same direction. There are, however, certain cases in which data for slightly different shapes can be correlated without much error. For example, in problems involving cylinders, although to maintain similarity of shape the ratio of d/l should be kept constant, for long cylinders, provided that end effects can be neglected or allowed for, length may be left out of account, and diameter taken as the characteristic linear dimension. Such cases will be considered in more detail as they arise.

Again, if a surface in contact with a fluid is rough, dimensional methods require that the magnitude of the surface irregularities should be in proportion to the sizes of body studied. In practice it is obviously not feasible, except in very artificial cases, to adhere to this requirement, and the effects of roughness upon heat transfer are usually expressed by ratio to the corresponding heat transfer for a smooth surface.

BIBLIOGRAPHY

DIMENSIONAL ANALYSIS OF CONVECTION

1. BRIDGMAN, P. W. *Dimensional Analysis* (Yale University Press, 1931).
2. BUCKINGHAM, E. 'On Physically Similar Systems: Illustrations of the Use of Dimensional Equations.' *Phys. Rev.* 1914, **4**, 345.
3. *Dictionary of Applied Physics*, vol. I: Dynamical Similarity, the Principles of.
4. NUSSELT, W. 'Der Einfluss der Gastemperatur auf den Wärmeübergang im Rohr.' *Tech. Mech. und Thermodynamik*, 1930, **1**, 277.

RELATION BETWEEN HEAT TRANSFER AND FRICTION

THERE is a close relation between the temperature distribution (and therefore the heat transfer) and the velocity distribution (and therefore the momentum transfer), near any surface over which a fluid at a different temperature is moving, particularly for flow through a pipe or over a plane surface. It is therefore important, before considering heat transfer by convection between surface and fluid, to know something of the mechanism of fluid flow. Most of the experiments on fluid flow have been carried out for isothermal conditions, but they can often be applied to cases where there is heat flow.

Turbulent and streamline flow. The steady motion of a fluid as given by the solution of the fundamental equations of viscous motion for any given boundary conditions is known as streamline, viscous, or laminar flow. In practice when the velocity exceeds a certain value, expressed as a critical value of a Reynolds number associated with the particular shapes of the fluid boundaries, the flow ceases to be steady and various flow phenomena occur associated with the formation of eddies or vortices which cause the general flow pattern to differ greatly from that of streamline flow. The term turbulent is applied to such flows generally, but there are many kinds of turbulence according to the size and intensity of the eddies and the general eddy distribution and degree of instability of the flow. In many instances conditions are attained where the average velocity at any point does not change with time, although the actual velocity fluctuates, and the flow pattern is one of 'steady' turbulent flow. It is not within the province of this book to consider the motion of fluids in any detail and the interested reader is referred to other works for such matters [1, 2]. Since, however, flow through a pipe is of special importance to engineers, it may be worth giving a short account of the elements of this particular flow.

The nature of the motion of a fluid flowing through a pipe depends essentially upon $v\rho d/\mu$, known as the Reynolds number, Re, already referred to in the chapter on dimensional analysis. When Re is below about 2,100, the motion is everywhere steady and is termed streamline, viscous, or laminar. When Re exceeds 2,100, the motion becomes unsteady and the fluid, except very near the walls of the pipe, breaks into eddies or vortices, and eventually reaches a steady turbulent condition, usually when Re exceeds about 3,000. If the flow at the entrance to a long,

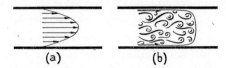

(a)   (b)

FIG. 21. Velocity distribution for flow through pipe:
(a) streamline; (b) turbulent.

smooth, straight pipe is turbulent, but Re is below the critical value, the flow a certain distance along the pipe will become laminar. On the other hand, if the flow at the entrance is laminar, but Re is above the critical value, the flow may not become turbulent unless there is some obstacle, change of direction, or the like, to upset it. Gibson [3], under careful conditions with a convergent pipe, was able to maintain laminar flow to Re 97,000. In short pipes there may not be length enough for the flow to change its character, when this at the inlet is not in accordance with Re, so that the flow may be turbulent throughout for Re less than 2,100, or streamline throughout for Re greater than 3,000.

The distribution of velocity along any pipe radius is not the same for streamline as for turbulent flow. The particles of fluid in contact with the pipe wall have zero velocity in both cases, and the flow extremely near a smooth pipe wall may also be taken as streamline in both cases, but for streamline flow across the entire pipe the velocity distribution curve is parabolic, whereas for fully turbulent flow the curve is steeper near the wall and flatter near the axis, as shown in Fig. 21.

For the most common cases in which the main stream is in

turbulent motion the change in the type of flow from pipe wall
to pipe axis is shown diagrammatically in Fig. 22. The space
may be regarded as divided into three regions, although in practice the boundaries between them are not discontinuities and
there is a gradual transition between one region and the next,
often with fluctuation. The fluid in immediate contact with the
wall AA has zero velocity and very near the wall in the region
between AA and BB is in streamline flow. The region between
BB and CC has been termed the buffer layer; in it the motion is

FIG. 22. Change from streamline to turbulent flow
between pipe wall and axis.

intermediate in character between the streamline region and the
region between CC and the pipe axis, in which turbulence is
always maintained. The thickness of the different zones of flow
depends upon the velocity of the main fluid stream and the
roughness of the pipe wall.

Pressure drop along a pipe. Since energy is dissipated as
heat when a viscous fluid is continuously sheared by passing it
through a pipe, power must be supplied to maintain the flow even
though the entrance and exit velocities are the same. This is
apparent in the drop of pressure along the pipe, the frictional
force being given by $\Delta p \times \pi d^2/4 = (F/g) \times \pi \, dl$ which, in dimensionless form, becomes

$$\Delta p = 8(F/\rho v^2)(l/d)(\rho v^2/2g) \text{ lb./ft.}^2 \text{ cross-section,} \qquad (32)$$

where v is expressed in ft./hr., g is the acceleration due to gravity,
$= 4{\cdot}18 \times 10^8$ ft./hr.², and F is the frictional force per sq. ft. of
pipe surface, having units lb. $\times g$/ft.² In industrial problems Δp
is usually given in in. of water and must then be multiplied by
$62{\cdot}4/12$ to bring it to lb./ft.² of cross-section before using expression (32).

A slightly different method of expression is often used, known as the Fanning equation, namely:

$$\Delta p = f(4l/d)(\rho v^2/2g) \text{ lb./ft.}^2, \qquad (33)$$

the friction factor f, in this equation obviously being equal to $2F/\rho v^2$.

The dimensionless group, $F/\rho v^2$, depends upon the Reynolds number and upon the surface roughness in relation to the pipe diameter, known as the 'relative roughness'. It has been

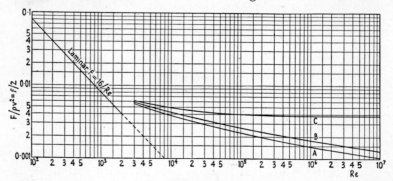

Fig. 23. Relation between Reynolds number and friction factor for flow of fluid through pipe. A, smooth; B, steel; C, cast iron.

determined experimentally by a number of workers for pipes of different diameters, different material, and different surface roughness, but there is wide variation in the results, and in any case it is not often possible to specify the condition of a surface with any accuracy. In Fig. 23, however, approximate values of $F/\rho v^2$ are shown for a range of Re for different types of pipe. In the transition region between streamline and turbulent flow the shape of the curves is uncertain.

For isothermal streamline flow, the pressure drop due to friction in a straight circular pipe, was derived by Poiseuille on the assumption that there is no slip of the fluid at the pipe surface. The expression thus obtained, which has been confirmed by experiment, is $\Delta p = 32\mu l v/g d^2 \text{ lb./ft.}^2$ (34)

This, with (32) or (33), gives respectively $F/\rho v^2 = 8/Re$, or $f = 16/Re$.

Pipes of non-circular cross-section. For pipes of rectangular, annular, or other cross-section the pressure drop for turbulent flow is given closely by that for a circular pipe of the same hydraulic diameter, that is (4 × area of cross-section)/ perimeter, except that for very flat pipes the friction may be abnormally high. The effect of roughness is also more marked for a channel that is very small in one dimension than for a circular channel of the same hydraulic diameter.

For streamline flow the expressions for non-circular channels are too complicated to be given here.

The pressure drop for the important case of fluids flowing across pipe banks will be dealt with later in the chapter on forced convection.

Relation between heat transfer and friction. Osborne Reynolds [4] in 1874 first drew attention to the similarity of the processes of heat transfer and friction between a surface and a fluid in turbulent motion. Suppose a fluid particle of mass m to move from the main fluid stream, having a velocity v, to the surface, at which it is reduced to rest. The momentum conveyed to the surface by the particle is mv. If the temperature difference between the main stream and the surface is θ, and assuming that the particle remains long enough in contact with the surface to attain the surface temperature, the heat transfer from fluid to surface is $mc\theta$. The ratio of the momentum transfer to the heat transfer is thus $v/c\theta$. Applying this argument to all the particles which move between the fluid and the surface in unit time, the ratio of the heat transfer per unit time to the friction drag force tangential to the surface (change of momentum parallel to the surface per unit time) is thus given by

$$\frac{H}{F} = \frac{c\theta}{v}. \tag{35}$$

In this equation H and F may refer to any area of surface and to unit area in particular. It is important to remember that F is force per unit area, i.e. lb. $\times g/\text{ft.}^2 = \text{lb./ft. hr.}^2$ Thus H becomes

$$\frac{\text{lb.}}{\text{ft. hr.}^2} \times \frac{\text{B.Th.U.}}{°\text{F. lb.}} \times \frac{\theta \times \text{hr.}}{\text{ft.}} = \text{B.Th.U./ft.}^2\text{ hr.},$$

which is correct.

Equation (35) is known as Reynolds's relation between heat transfer and friction, and is very useful for calculating heat transfer from friction values or vice versa. The above is a simple account of its derivation. For a more formal derivation in terms of turbulent motion theory see *Modern Developments in Fluid Dynamics* [1], vol. ii, pp. 649, 654.

Taylor-Prandtl refinement of Reynolds's relation. Reynolds's formula takes no account of the thermal conductivity of the fluid, assuming the mechanism of heat transfer to be that of turbulent or eddying flow. In practice, as the surface is approached the turbulent motion at right angles to it must decrease, and the heat transfer across the layers of fluid nearest the surface is by thermal conduction. Hence Reynolds's assumption that the particles of fluid reach the surface, at which they are reduced to rest, and attain the surface temperature is not fulfilled in practice.

Later, Prandtl [5] in Germany and Taylor [6] in England pointed out that a closer approximation to the true state of affairs could be obtained by imagining the fluid to be divided into two regions, a 'boundary layer' between the surface and an imaginary plane parallel to it at a distance x away, in which the motion is assumed streamline, and the region outside to which the Reynolds theory may then be applied with less risk of error. Across the boundary layer heat is transferred by thermal conduction, and momentum by the normal process of viscous drag in a shearing fluid.

Thus, assuming the velocity at the imaginary plane to be av, and the temperature $b\theta$, where a and b are both less than unity

(see diagram), the Reynolds relation applied to the region outside and up to the imaginary plane gives

$$H/F = c(\theta - b\theta)/(v - av). \tag{36}$$

The heat transfer across the boundary layer is $kb\theta/x$ and the friction drag by viscosity, $\mu av/x$, where μ is the viscosity. Hence, since H and F are the same for either region, the conditions being steady,

$$H/F = kb\theta/\mu av. \tag{37}$$

Equating (36) and (37) gives

$$(c\mu/k)(1-b)a = b(1-a) \quad \text{or} \quad b/a = Pr/[1+a(Pr-1)]. \tag{38}$$

Substituting for b in (37) then gives

$$\frac{H}{F} = \frac{c\theta}{v} \frac{1}{1+a\{(c\mu/k)-1\}} = \frac{c\theta}{v} \frac{1}{1+a(Pr-1)}, \tag{39}$$

which is the Taylor-Prandtl equation, containing the unknown ratio and the ratio of the velocity at the imaginary plane between the turbulent and non-turbulent regions to the main stream velocity. Experiments show that a is usually between 0·4 and 0·6. It will be noted that if Pr is unity, (39) reduces to the original Reynolds equation (35), and since for gases Pr varies only between 0·65 and 1, the difference between the two equations is not very great. For liquids, however, Pr is much greater and the Taylor-Prandtl equation gives a much lower ratio of heat transfer to friction than the Reynolds equation.

Limiting cases of streamline flow only and turbulent flow only. If $a = 0$, that is if the conditions at the imaginary plane are assumed the same as at the surface, (39) reduces to Reynolds's original form, as would be expected. On the other hand, if $a = 1$, that is if the non-turbulent layer extends right across the stream to where the velocity is v, (39) becomes

$$\frac{H}{F} = \frac{c\theta}{v} \times \frac{1}{Pr} = \frac{k\theta}{\mu v}, \tag{40}$$

which is the Reynolds relation adapted to purely streamline flow.

Case of $Pr = 1$. When $Pr = 1$, expressions (40) for purely streamline flow and (35) for purely turbulent flow become identical.

It may be noted from (38) that when $Pr = 1$, b becomes equal to a, showing that the temperature difference across the boundary layer is the same proportion of the total temperature difference as the velocity difference across the boundary layer is of the total velocity difference. This explains physically why the original Reynolds equation agrees well with experiment for gases, since the ratio of H to F is the same whether reckoned for the streamline boundary layer or for the outer turbulent zone, or for both in series.

Many actual measurements of the temperature and velocity distribution have been made for air flowing through heated pipes and along heated plane surfaces, and it has been found that if v/v_{max} and θ/θ_{max} are plotted against distance from surface they both lie almost on the same curve.

Other workers have introduced further refinements into the heat transfer-friction relation including allowance for a third or buffer layer, as in Fig. 22. Their expressions, though more complicated, are still not in close agreement with experiment, and the original Reynolds expression is in many cases accurate enough and more convenient for use for gases in heat transfer work. It follows from (35) that $F/\rho v^2 = H/c\theta\rho v$, the 'Stanton' number, St. Hence the friction curves of Fig. 23 can be used directly to predict the heat transfer for gases flowing through pipes. But it must be remembered that an increase in friction due to roughness is not necessarily accompanied by a proportional increase in heat transfer. This is because, whereas for smooth surfaces the whole of the pressure drop is balanced by skin friction, for rough surfaces some of the resistance to flow is caused by form drag.

For liquids the Taylor-Prandtl refinement should be used because the higher values of Pr make the two expressions differ considerably. Note also from (38) that as Pr gets larger b becomes greater relative to a, until for very large Pr, b approaches unity, showing that the temperature of the imaginary plane approaches that of the main fluid. In other words, practically the whole temperature drop is taken up across the boundary layer, leaving only a small drop across the turbulent outer regions, as would be expected from the poor conductivity of liquids having high Pr values.

Another difficulty with liquids is the temperature variation of viscosity, and many formulae outside the scope of this book have been proposed to allow for this.

Formulae in terms of pressure drop along a pipe. The pressure drop p_1-p_2 between sections of a uniform pipe of cross-section S and perimeter P at distance l apart is related to the friction force F, assuming constant velocity, by

$$(p_1-p_2)S = FPl,$$

or, using the hydraulic mean diameter d, defined by $d = (4S/P)$,

$$p_1-p_2 = \frac{4l}{d} F, \tag{41}$$

which gives F in terms of pressure drop.

The temperature rise t_2-t_1 of the fluid is related to the heat transfer by

$$\rho v S c(t_2-t_1) = HPl, \tag{42}$$

and putting $P = 4S/d$,

$$t_2-t_1 = \frac{4l}{d} \frac{H}{\rho v c}. \tag{43}$$

Dividing (43) by (41) and substituting for H/F from the Reynolds formula (35),

$$\frac{t_2-t_1}{p_1-p_2} = \frac{\theta}{\rho v^2} = \frac{1}{2} \times \frac{\text{temperature difference surface to fluid}}{\text{dynamic head}}. \tag{44}$$

Strictly speaking, (44) assumes the temperature rise (t_2-t_1) to be small compared with the temperature difference θ, otherwise θ will vary along the pipe, which must then be divided into sections for calculation purposes. Equation (44) is, however, very convenient, showing that the ratio $(t_2-t_1)/\theta$, i.e. of temperature rise to temperature difference, is half the ratio $(p_1-p_2)/(\frac{1}{2}\rho v^2)$, i.e. half the ratio of pressure drop to dynamic head.

The Taylor-Prandtl formula may similarly be written

$$\frac{t_2-t_1}{p_1-p_2} = \frac{\theta}{\rho v^2} \times \frac{1}{1+a(Pr-1)}. \tag{45}$$

Yet another form of the heat transfer-friction relation is in terms of the drag coefficient defined in aerodynamics as equal to

$F/\frac{1}{2}\rho v^2$, and the heat transfer factor or Stanton number

$$\frac{H}{cv\theta\rho} = \frac{Nu}{(Re\ Pr)}.$$

By (35) it easily follows that the Stanton number equals half the drag coefficient.

EXAMPLE 1

Air at 300° F. enters a pipe of inner diameter 2 in. at 20 ft./sec., the drop of static pressure along the pipe being 0·02 in. water per foot length. If the surface of the pipe is kept at 80° F., calculate the temperature of the air 1 ft. along the pipe, using the Reynolds relation $H/F = c\theta/v$ (see p. 81). The density of air at N.T.P. is 0·08 lb./ft.³

Solution. Pressure drop for 1 ft. length of pipe = 0·02 in.

water $= \dfrac{0\cdot02 \times 62\cdot4}{12}$ lb./ft.² =, for cross-section πr^2,

$$\frac{0\cdot02 \times 62\cdot4}{12} \times \pi r^2 \text{ lb.}$$

Thus F', the frictional force per foot length,

$$= \frac{0\cdot02 \times 62\cdot4}{12} \times \pi r^2 g \text{ poundals.}$$

Hence H', the heat transfer per foot length,

$$= \frac{0\cdot02 \times 62\cdot4 \times \pi r^2 g}{12} \times \frac{c \times \theta}{20 \times 60 \times 60} \frac{\text{B.Th.U.}}{\text{ft. length hr.}}.$$

Heat capacity of air

$$= 20 \times 60 \times 60 \times \pi r^2 \times 0\cdot08 \times c \times (492/760) \text{ B.Th.U./°F. hr.}$$

Hence, temperature drop of air, based on initial temperature difference of $(300-80) = 220$ F.°,

$$= \frac{0\cdot02 \times 62\cdot4 \times \pi r^2 \times 32 \times 60^4 \times c \times 220 \times 760}{12 \times 20 \times 60^2 \times 20 \times 60^2 \times \pi r^2 \times 0\cdot08 \times c \times 492} = 34\cdot3 \text{ degrees.}$$

A slight adjustment should now be made, since the mean temperature difference has been taken too high. If a mean temperature difference of 204 F.° is taken, the temperature drop of the air would be $(204/220) \times 34\cdot3 = 31\cdot8$ F.° This would give a mean temperature difference of $\dfrac{300+(300-32)}{2} - 80 = 204$

degrees, so evidently the correct answer is a temperature drop of 32 degrees, giving an air temperature of $(300-32) = 268°$ F. 1 ft. along the pipe.

EXAMPLE 2

It is required to heat 1,570 ft.^{3} of air per hour from 60° F. to 100° F. by passing it through a pipe of inner diameter 1 in. maintained at 212° F. What length of pipe and pressure head in inches of water will be needed?

Solution. Cross-section of pipe $= \dfrac{22}{7} \times \dfrac{1}{24 \times 24} = 0 \cdot 00545$ ft.^{2}

Velocity of air at 60° F. $= \dfrac{1570}{0 \cdot 00545 \times 60 \times 60} = 80$ ft./sec.

∴ From Fig. 34, coefficient of convection

$$= 17 \cdot 7 \text{ B.Th.U./ft.}^2 \text{ hr. °F.}$$

From Table XVIII, specific heat of air at 60° F. $= 0 \cdot 0184$ B.Th.U./ft.^{3} °F.

Hence, working on a mean temperature difference of $(212-80)$ $= 132$ F.°, the area of pipe needed $= \dfrac{1570 \times 40 \times 0 \cdot 0184}{17 \cdot 7 \times 132}$ ft.^{2}, and

length of pipe needed $= \dfrac{1570 \times 40 \times 0 \cdot 0184 \times 7 \times 12}{17 \cdot 7 \times 132 \times 22} = 1 \cdot 88$ ft.

The frictional force for the whole pipe will be given by $H'v/c\theta$ lb. ft./hr.^{2}, or $H'v/c\theta g$ lb., where H' is the heat transfer per hour for the whole pipe, g is 32×60^4 ft./hr.^{2}, and c is the specific heat of air in B.Th.U./lb. °F. $= 0 \cdot 24$.

Hence the frictional force in lb. per ft.^{2} cross-section

$$= H'v/(c\theta g \times \pi r^2) \text{ lb./ft.}^2$$

$$= \frac{H'v \times 12}{c\theta g \times \pi r^2 \times 62 \cdot 4} \text{ in. water}$$

$$= \frac{1570 \times 40 \times 0 \cdot 0184 \times 80 \times 60 \times 60 \times 12 \times 7 \times 24 \times 24}{0 \cdot 24 \times 132 \times 32 \times 60 \times 60 \times 60 \times 60 \times 22 \times 62 \cdot 4}$$

$$= 0 \cdot 88 \text{ in. water.}$$

BIBLIOGRAPHY

RELATION BETWEEN HEAT TRANSFER AND FRICTION

1. GOLDSTEIN, S. *Modern Developments in Fluid Dynamics* (Oxford University Press, 1938).
2. DURAND, H. F. *Aerodynamic Theory* (Julius Springer, 1934).
3. GIBSON, A. H. 'On the Flow of Water through Pipes and Passages having Convergent and Divergent Boundaries.' *Proc. Roy. Soc. A*, 1910, **83**, 376.
4. REYNOLDS, O. 'Extent and Action of the Heating Surface of Steam Boilers.' *Proc. Manchester Lit. Phil. Soc.* 1874, **14**, 7.
5. PRANDTL, L. 'Bemerkung über den Wärmeübergang im Rohr.' *Phys. Z.* 1928, **29**, 487. Also 'Eine Beziehung zwischen Wärme-austauch und Strömungswiderstand der Flüssigkeiten.' *Z. Phys.* 1910, **11**, 1072.
6. TAYLOR, G. I. 'Conditions at the Surface of a Hot Body exposed to the Wind.' *Brit. Advisory Comm. Aeronautics, Rept. & Memo.* 1916, **2**, 423 (N. 272).

NATURAL CONVECTION

It has already been explained, in the chapter on dimensional analysis of convection, that natural convection is the term used to denote the heat transfer between a surface and a fluid, when the convective movements are brought about solely by differences of density caused by differences of temperature. It was shown also that natural convection heat transfer can be expressed by relating $Hl/k\theta$, the Nusselt number (Nu), to $ag\theta l^3\rho^2/\mu^2$, the Grashof number (Gr), and $c\mu/k$, the Prandtl number (Pr).

Theory indicates that, unless Pr is very small, only the product $(Gr\ Pr) = ag\theta cl^3\rho^2/k\mu$ need be considered provided the fluid currents are slow enough for the inertia stresses to be negligible compared with viscous stresses. It is in fact found that for streamline flow the results are well expressed in terms of $(Gr\ Pr)$. Since for gases Pr varies only within very narrow limits, it could, if desired, be cut out of the correlations. Actually it is convenient to present the results for both gases and liquids in terms of $(Gr\ Pr)$; except for liquid metals for which, owing to their high thermal conductivity and low specific heat, Pr is extremely low, the results for all fluids should then lie almost on the same curve. It will be seen later that they do in fact conform to this expectation. Experiments show also that the relation holds for gases at pressures above or below atmospheric, ρ of course, for a perfect gas, being directly proportional to the pressure. The coefficient of expansion, a, for a gas increases with increasing pressure, and there is also known to be a corresponding slight increase in the specific heat, c. The values of the thermal conductivity, k, and viscosity, μ, at extreme pressures are very uncertain, but there is evidence that they also increase with increasing pressure, in such a way that $c\mu/k$ remains nearly constant. The net effect upon the heat transfer by natural convection of variations in the physical constants other than ρ with pressure is, however, not rapid; for air at temperatures around 100° F., for instance, an increase of about 10 per cent. is caused by an increase in pressure from 1 to 50 atmospheres. Provided the correct value is taken for ρ, therefore, sufficiently accurate estimates can often be obtained by taking the other quantities involved, i.e. a, c, k, and μ at atmospheric pressure, as given in Table XVIII.

When the convection currents become fully turbulent theory indicates that it should be permissible to omit the viscosity terms in the groups concerned and that Nu should be related to $(Gr\ Pr^2)$, i.e. to $(Gr\ Pr) \times Pr = ag\theta c^2 l^3 \rho^2/k^2$. Unfortunately few of the experiments have extended far into the turbulent region except for air; but, as will be seen later, results for vertical surfaces in air, water, and ethylene glycol, covering a range of Pr from about 0·7 to 118, indicate that for values of $(Gr\ Pr)$ between 10^{10} and 10^{12} the appropriate power of Pr is between 1 and 2. This is probably because, although turbulence for vertical surfaces in air is known to set in at $(Gr\ Pr)$ about 10^9, even at values of 10^9 to 10^{12} it is still fully developed only at the upper parts of the surface.

The temperature of the fluid in immediate contact with a warm surface is of course the same as that of the surface, but it decreases very sharply through the thin layer of nearly stagnant fluid found very near to the surface, which is known as the 'boundary layer', through which the heat has to be transferred by conduction. It then decreases less quickly to the bulk temperature of the surrounding fluid. When reference is made to the temperature of a fluid it is always this bulk temperature which is meant unless otherwise stated. In determining θ, the temperature difference between surface and fluid, the bulk temperature of the fluid well away from the surface must likewise be taken.

In all cases of natural convection, whether for gases or liquids, the values of the physical constants c, ρ, k, and μ are to be taken at the arithmetic mean temperature of surface and bulk fluid, usually known as the 'film' temperature, t_f. For gases, the coefficient of expansion, a, as already explained on p. 73 is given by $1/T_g$. Liquids have a much smaller coefficient of expansion than gases, and the range of θ is also much smaller. In general the coefficient of expansion of liquids increases with increase of temperature, but, assuming a linear law of variation over the interval θ, a may be taken as $\dfrac{1}{V}\dfrac{dV}{dt}$ equal to $-\dfrac{1}{\rho}\dfrac{d\rho}{dt}$ at the film temperature.

The only shapes that have been studied in any detail in both

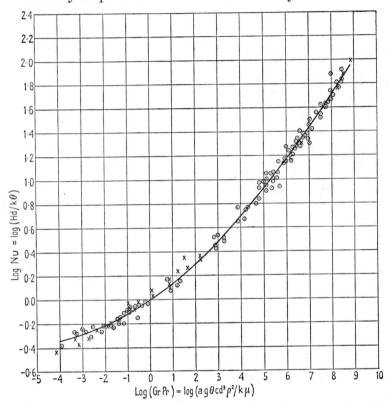

FIG. 24. Natural convection for horizontal cylinders. ⊙s are experimental points for gases, ×s are experimental points for liquids.

gases and liquids are horizontal cylinders and vertical plane surfaces. There are also some results for vertical cylinders, and for horizontal surfaces facing upwards and downwards, in air. Otherwise only very scattered information is available. The surfaces investigated were in all cases hotter than the surrounding fluid.

Long horizontal or vertical cylinders. Fig. 24, in which

$\log Nu$ is plotted against $\log(Gr\ Pr)$, shows the results for horizontal cylinders, long in the sense that the ratio of length to diameter is large, in gases and liquids. They extend, with diameter taken as the characteristic linear dimension, to $(Gr\ Pr)$ about 10^9. A few results for long vertical cylinders in gases, which, within the limits of experimental uncertainty, agree with those for horizontal cylinders, are included. The gases used were air, hydrogen, and carbon dioxide with cylinder diameters 0·0015 to 10 in., temperature differences from a few degrees to nearly 3,000 F.° and pressures from a few inches of mercury to over 100 atmospheres. The points for liquids are for alcohol, aniline, carbon tetrachloride, glycerine, olive oil, and water, for diameters 0·0033 to 2 in., and temperature differences up to about 150 F.°

It will be seen that the experimental points for gases and liquids fall well on the same curve, and, as has already been said, theory indicates that so long as the flow is streamline, that is, for horizontal cylinders, so long as $(Gr\ Pr)$ does not exceed about 10^8, they should not differ. When $(Gr\ Pr)$ exceeds 10^8, turbulence is known to occur along the top of a horizontal cylinder, spreading downwards as $(Gr\ Pr)$ increases.

Vertical plane surfaces, or vertical cylinders of large diameter. Fig. 25 shows the corresponding curve for vertical surfaces in air, which extends to $(Gr\ Pr)$ above 10^{11}, the height of the surface being taken as the appropriate linear dimension in calculating Nu and Pr. For comparison, points for water, oil, and carbon tetrachloride for $(Gr\ Pr)$ up to the limit of the streamline region, i.e. about 2×10^9, have been included, and fall on the same curve. The results for gases are all for air, the surface heights going up to 13 ft., the temperature differences to more than 1,000 F.°, and the pressures to 65 atmospheres. A few points for vertical cylinders of diameter above 2·5 in., for which the heat transfer is the same as for vertical planes, have been included. For liquids the heights extend only up to 1 ft. and the temperature differences to 15 F.°

For full turbulence, as already mentioned, according to theory Nu for natural convection should correlate with $(Gr\ Pr^2)$, in which the viscosity term disappears. Unfortunately there are few data at high values of $(Gr\ Pr)$, but Saunders's [1] results for a vertical plane surface in air and water, and Touloukian's [2]

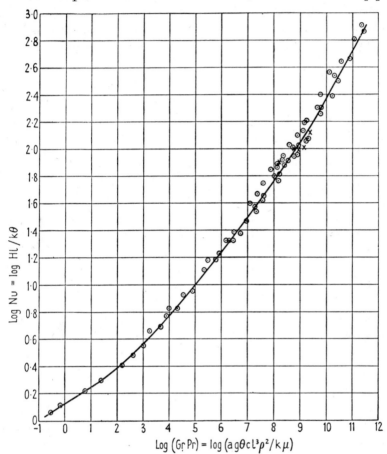

FIG. 25. Natural convection for vertical surfaces. ⊙s are experimental points for gases, ×s are experimental points for liquids.

for a vertical cylinder of diameter 3 in. in water and ethylene glycol, extend to values of $(Gr\ Pr)$ of 10^{11} to 10^{12}. This is considerably beyond the onset of turbulence, which Saunders found by an optical method to begin at $(Gr\ Pr) = 2 \times 10^9$. As would perhaps be expected, in the region between about 10^{10} and 10^{12}

the results point to a relation of Nu with $(Gr\ Pr^n)$, where n is between 1 and 2. Saunders's and Touloukian's results cannot conveniently be shown on the same diagram as they differ considerably for water, but they are shown separately in Figs. 26 *a* and 26 *b*, in which $\log Nu$ is still plotted against $\log(Gr\ Pr)$.

It will be seen that Saunders's results for water and air are

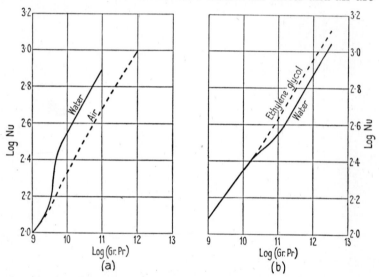

FIG. 26. Natural convection from vertical surfaces to fluids at high values of $(Gr\ Pr)$: (a) water and air; (b) ethylene glycol and water.

coincident at $(Gr\ Pr)$ of 10^9, but then diverge, the water results becoming about 50 per cent. higher than the air results for $(Gr\ Pr)$ above 10^{10}. In this region, for any given value of $\log Nu$, $\log(Gr\ Pr)$ is about 0·5 less for water than for air. In the water experiments, Pr was about 7·4, in the air experiments about 0·74, a ratio of 10:1. Hence, if $\log Nu$ were plotted against $\log(Gr\ Pr^{1·5})$, instead of against $\log(Gr\ Pr)$, the results for water and air would be brought on to the same curve.

From Fig. 26 *b* it will be seen that Touloukian's results for ethylene glycol and water agree at $(Gr\ Pr)$ of 10^9, but that above 10^{10} the results for ethylene glycol are about 20 per cent. higher than those for water. His experiments covered a wider range of temperature than Saunders's, so that Pr also varied considerably for both liquids, but was higher for ethylene glycol, for which the top value was 118. The results for values of $(Gr\ Pr)$ above 10^{10} were brought into coincidence by plotting $\log Nu$ against $\log(Gr\ Pr^{1\cdot3})$. Results for taller surfaces, and consequently

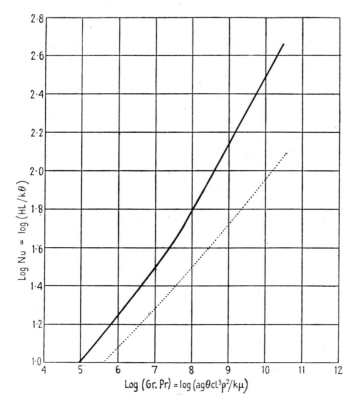

Fig. 27. Natural convection for horizontal plane surfaces in air.
———————— facing upwards, ... facing downwards.

increased values of Gr, for which the appropriate power of Pr in the correlations should approach 2, would be of interest.

For water in the turbulent region for $(Gr\ Pr)$ above 2×10^9 Saunders's results, which are probably the more reliable, are well expressed by

$$Nu = 0\cdot17(Gr\ Pr)^{0\cdot33}. \tag{46}$$

Horizontal plane surface facing upwards. In Fig. 27 the

experimental curve for natural convection is shown for warm horizontal plane surfaces facing upwards in cooler air, the only fluid for which there are yet results. In this case the characteristic linear dimension taken in Nu and Gr is the side length. In most of the experiments the surfaces used were square, or nearly square, but if they were rectangular a mean value was taken for the side length. The maximum size investigated is about 2 ft., with temperature differences between surface and air going up to over 1,000 F.° Turbulent conditions are found to begin in this case at lower values of $(Gr\ Pr)$ than for the other shapes.

Horizontal plane surfaces facing downwards. Fig. 27 shows also the results for warm horizontal plane surfaces facing downwards in air. In this case, were it not for edge effects and slight irregularities of temperature over the plate surface, since the layer of warm air near the plate would be in equilibrium in a draught-free room, there would be no convection currents, although heat would of course still be lost from the plate by conduction. Actually there is always some air movement, but the conditions are known to be streamline throughout the experimental range, which extends to values of $(Gr\ Pr)$ above 10^{10}.

Discussion of curves. It will be noticed that the curves of $\log Nu$ against $\log(Gr\ Pr)$ are all of nearly the same form, their slope gradually increasing as $(Gr\ Pr)$ increases. For $(Gr\ Pr)$ between 10^5 and 10^8 the slope is in all cases $\frac{1}{4}$, and when $(Gr\ Pr)$ exceeds 10^8 or 10^9 it becomes about $\frac{1}{3}$, indicating that Nu is proportional to $(Gr\ Pr)^{1/3}$, and therefore that, apart from any slight effect due to changes in the values of the physical constants with temperature, the heat transfer for any given temperature difference should be independent of size, l, since Hl/θ is proportional to $(l^3)^{1/3}$, i.e. to l. The warm horizontal surfaces facing downwards, for which turbulence is not reached, are an exception, and the slope of the log curves to the highest values of $(Gr\ Pr)$ investigated, i.e. over 10^{10}, is still in this case only about $\frac{1}{4}$.

Except for small temperature differences, say below 10 F.°, $(Gr\ Pr)$ for gases will exceed 10^5 for l above about 2 in. and the regions of $(Gr\ Pr)$ below this refer mainly to heat transfer from wires, or from larger surfaces in gases at low pressure. The range of $(Gr\ Pr)$ from 10^5 to 10^8 corresponds to a range of l about 2 in. to 2 ft. in gases at atmospheric pressure, so that practically all the results for cylinders, with d as the characteristic linear dimension, are in the streamline range. For vertical surfaces, with results to heights of 13 ft., the curves extend well into the turbulent region. In liquids turbulence is reached at much smaller sizes, but the range of temperature difference encountered is also much smaller; results for cylinders may thus still lie in the streamline range, but for the biggest size investigated, i.e. a cylinder of 2 in. diameter in water, $(Gr\ Pr)$ exceeded 10^8 when θ exceeded roughly 20 F.°

The equations to the curves for gases or liquids in the streamline range of $(Gr\ Pr)$ greater than 10^5 are

$$Nu = C(Gr\ Pr)^{0 \cdot 25}, \tag{47}$$

and for gases in the turbulent range

$$Nu = C'(Gr\ Pr)^{0 \cdot 33}, \tag{48}$$

where C and C', constants depending on the geometrical conditions, are given in Table IV.

TABLE IV. *Values of Constants for Expressions (47) and (48)*

	C	C'
Horizontal or vertical cylinders: Characteristic linear dimension, diameter	0·47	0·10
Vertical planes, or vertical cylinders of large diameter: Characteristic linear dimension, height .	0·56	0·12
Horizontal planes facing upwards: Characteristic linear dimension, side	0·54	0·14
Horizontal planes facing downwards: Characteristic linear dimension, side	0·25	1/3 slope not reached

It is evident that the process of heat loss by natural convection from a horizontal plane surface facing upwards in a cooler fluid is, for the same temperature difference and the same film temperature, akin to that of heat gain from a similar surface facing downwards in a hotter fluid, except for the difference in the coefficient of expansion for gases, which is inversely proportional to the absolute temperature of the gas. The expressions for a hot surface facing upwards must therefore be used in calculating the heat transfer to a cool surface facing downwards, and the expressions for a hot surface facing downwards for the heat transfer to a cool surface facing upwards.

Simplification of expressions for natural convection in air. In the streamline region for $(Gr\,Pr)$ greater than 10^5, since from (47),

$$Hl/k\theta = C(ag\theta cl^3\rho^2/k\mu)^{0\cdot25}, \quad H = C\times(k/l)(agcl^3\rho^2/k\mu)^{0\cdot25}\theta^{1\cdot25}.$$

If this is evaluated for air, it is found that up to surface temperatures of $1,500°$ F. or more, H is nearly equal to $0\cdot50C\times(\theta^{1\cdot25}/l^{0\cdot25})$ B.Th.U./ft.^{2} hr. Hence H/θ, $= \alpha$, the heat transfer coefficient, is equal to $0\cdot50C(\theta/l)^{0\cdot25}$ B.Th.U./ft.^{2} hr. °F.

In the turbulent region, since for gases from (48)

$$Hl/k\theta = C'(ag\theta cl^3\rho^2/k\mu)^{0\cdot33},$$
$$H = C'\times k(agc\rho^2/k\mu)^{0\cdot33}\theta^{0\cdot08}\theta^{1\cdot25},$$

which, on working out for air, is found for the same temperature range to be nearly equal to $2\cdot5C'\theta^{1\cdot25}$ B.Th.U./ft.^{2} hr. Hence H/θ, $= \alpha$, the heat transfer coefficient, is equal to $2\cdot5C'\theta^{0\cdot25}$.

The resulting simplified expressions given below are applicable without significant error to carbon monoxide, nitrogen, oxygen, or flue gases as well as to air. For hydrogen, which has a very high thermal conductivity, the heat transfer for any given shape and temperature conditions would be much greater.

TABLE V. *Simplified Expressions for Natural Convection in Air*

	Streamline region $(Gr\,Pr) > 10^4$ or 10^5		Turbulent region $(Gr\,Pr) > 10^8$ or 10^9	
	H B.Th.U. ft.^{2} hr.	$H/\theta = \alpha$ B.Th.U. ft.^{2} hr. °F.	H B.Th.U. ft.^{2} hr.	$H/\theta = \alpha$ B.Th.U. ft.^{2} hr. °F.
Horizontal or vertical cylinders (characteristic linear dimension diameter d).	$\dfrac{0\cdot24\theta^{1\cdot25}}{d^{0\cdot25}}$	$0\cdot24\left(\dfrac{\theta}{d}\right)^{0\cdot25}$	$0\cdot25\theta^{1\cdot25}$	$0\cdot25\theta^{0\cdot25}$
Vertical planes or vertical cylinders of large diameter (characteristic linear dimension height l).	$\dfrac{0\cdot28\theta^{1\cdot25}}{l^{0\cdot25}}$	$0\cdot28\left(\dfrac{\theta}{l}\right)^{0\cdot25}$	$0\cdot30\theta^{1\cdot25}$	$0\cdot30\theta^{0\cdot25}$
Horizontal planes facing upwards (characteristic linear dimension side l).	$\dfrac{0\cdot27\theta^{1\cdot25}}{l^{0\cdot25}}$	$0\cdot27\left(\dfrac{\theta}{l}\right)^{0\cdot25}$	$0\cdot35\theta^{1\cdot25}$	$0\cdot35\theta^{0\cdot25}$
Horizontal planes facing downwards (characteristic linear dimension side l).	$\dfrac{0\cdot12\theta^{1\cdot25}}{l^{0\cdot25}}$	$0\cdot12\left(\dfrac{\theta}{l}\right)^{0\cdot25}$		

Since the expressions above indicate that in the turbulent region natural convection from vertical surfaces is not far from the mean for horizontal surfaces facing upwards and downwards, it is usually good enough when dealing with complete bodies of linear dimensions above about a foot, whatever their shape, to take a mean value of $0.30\theta^{1.25}$ B.Th.U./ft.^{2} hr.

Curves showing values of $\theta^{1.25}$ for a range of θ from 0 to 2,000 are given in Fig. 28. In Table XVII the heat transfer H and coefficients of heat transfer α, by natural convection and radiation together in surroundings at 65° F., are given for surfaces of different emissivities, as calculated from the expressions

$$H = 0.30(t-65)^{1.25} + 1.73 \times 10^{-9} E(T^4 - 525^4) \frac{\text{B.Th.U.}}{\text{ft.}^2 \text{ hr.}}, \quad (49)$$

and
$$\alpha = H/\theta = H/(t-65) \frac{\text{B.Th.U.}}{\text{ft.}^2 \text{ hr. °F.}}. \quad (50)$$

NATURAL CONVECTION BETWEEN TWO PARALLEL SURFACES

The transfer of heat across a layer of fluid from a hotter to a colder surface is an interesting particular case of natural convection, the most important shapes being parallel planes and concentric cylinders. It would be expected that the results would differ according to whether the layers were open or closed at the edges, but most of the experimental work has been for closed layers.

Characteristic linear dimensions. For plane layers, the shape, strictly speaking, is determined by the ratios of the lengths of side of the plane l to the distance apart δ, and convection would be expected to depend upon l/δ as well as upon δ. Above a certain value, however, the effect of l dies out and, with δ, the distance apart, taken as the characteristic linear dimension, $Nu, = H\delta/k\theta$, can be related simply to $(Gr\ Pr), = ag\theta c\delta^3\rho^2/k\mu$, as in the cases of natural convection previously dealt with. Most of the experimental work has, in fact, been done for layers large compared with δ, and δ has been the variable.

In this special case of heat transfer across layers of fluid the temperature difference, θ, to be taken in Nu and Gr is not, as for a single plane surface, that between surface and fluid, but the

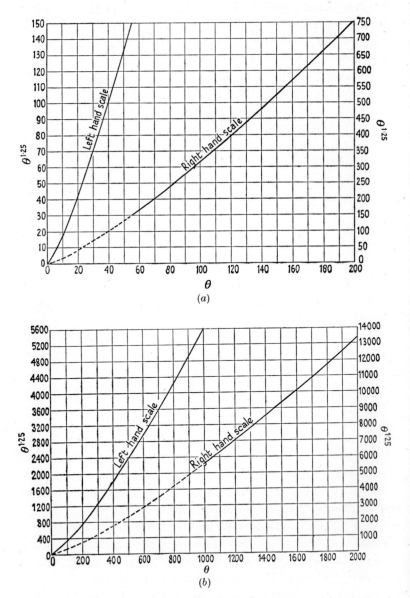

FIG. 28. Values of $\theta^{1\cdot25}$ (a) for θ up to 200° F.; (b) for θ up to 2,000° F.

full temperature difference between the two surfaces. And it should be noted that $Nu, = H\delta/k\theta, = H/H_k$, where H_k is the heat which would be transmitted per unit area per unit time by pure conduction across the layer for a temperature difference θ.

For long cylindrical layers the shape is determined by the

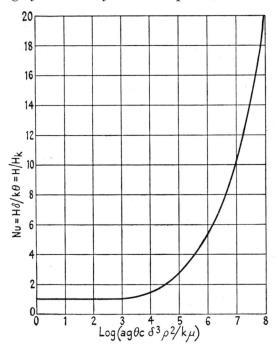

FIG. 29. Natural convection across a fluid layer between two parallel vertical plane surfaces, closed at the edges.

ratio d_o/d_i of the outer and inner diameters; hence, taking d_i as the characteristic linear dimension, $Nu, = Hd_i/k\theta$, should depend upon $(Gr\ Pr), = ag\theta cd_i^3\rho^2/k\mu$, and d_o/d_i.

Fluid layers between two parallel plane surfaces. Fig. 29 shows, as an example, the mean curve for large vertical plane layers, with $Nu, = H/H_k$, plotted against $\log(Gr\ Pr)$. It will be seen that, until $(Gr\ Pr)$ exceeds 10^3, the heat transfer is the same as would be calculated on the basis of pure conduction. The meaning of this is, of course, that in this region of very narrow layers natural convection currents are suppressed. As $(Gr\ Pr)$

increases above 10^3 they gradually become more active, and the heat transfer more and more exceeds that due to pure conduction. For $(Gr\ Pr)$ between about 10^4 and 10^6 the equation to the curve is

$$Nu = H\delta/k\theta = H/H_k = 0.15(Gr\ Pr)^{0.25}. \tag{51}$$

For still higher values of $(Gr\ Pr)$ the slope of the curve becomes $1/3$, showing that the heat transfer has become independent of δ; in other words, that the spacing has become so wide that the effect of either surface upon convection from the other has become negligible. In this region the equation to the mean curve is

$$Nu = H\delta/k\theta = H/H_k = 0.05(Gr\ Pr)^{0.33}, \tag{52}$$

and the heat transfer should be the same as that calculated from (48) for natural convection from a single tall vertical surface, remembering that in (48) the temperature difference is that from surface to fluid. Neglecting slight differences in the heat transfer coefficients from the hot surface to the mid-fluid, and from the mid-fluid to the cold surface, due to the different absolute temperatures, the mid-fluid must be at a temperature midway between that of the two surfaces. Using expression (48), with a halved temperature difference for calculating the heat transfer, which is proportional to $\theta^{1.33}$,

$$Nu = \frac{0.12}{2^{1.33}}(Gr\ Pr)^{0.33} = 0.05(Gr\ Pr)^{0.33},$$

i.e. (52).

From the results for vertical surfaces of height h with different h/δ ratios, Jakob [3] concluded that the heat transfer was proportional to $(h/\delta)^{-1/9}$. Thus, assuming that the limiting value has been reached when h/δ exceeds about 25, which is in rough agreement with experiment, the expressions above would need multiplying by $(25\delta/h)^{1/9}$ for lower values of h/δ.

For horizontal layers with the cooler surface uppermost the heat transfer is, as would be expected, greater than for vertical layers, but the excess found by different workers varies widely, say from 30 to 60 per cent.; in the region of 0.33 slope, however, the difference should be the same as that between natural convection from a single vertical surface and a single horizontal surface, i.e. barely 20 per cent. (see Table IV).

Theoretically, a horizontal layer of fluid with the hotter surface uppermost should be stable, and heat transferred by conduction only, whatever the value of δ. But actually, edge effects and non-uniformity of surface temperature may cause circulation in wide layers, with consequent increase in heat transfer.

It will be noticed that, for all the cases of heat transfer across plane fluid layers, so long as Nu is proportional to $(Gr\,Pr)^{0.25}$, H/θ will vary with $1/\delta^{0.25}$. Hence, as δ increases, H/θ will decrease until, when Nu becomes proportional to $(Gr\,Pr)^{0.33}$, it reaches a final minimum value. This means that, although the thermal conductivity of air is very low, a single air layer would not usually be an effective insulator, because before it becomes an inch thick convection sets in and the heat transfer cannot be much further reduced. On the other hand, if the single air layer were divided by parallel surfaces into a series of layers each so thin that the heat transfer across them was by conduction only, the heat transfer for any given temperature difference between the two outside surfaces would continue to decrease indefinitely with increase of thickness; the exchange of heat by radiation would at the same time be greatly decreased. This is, of course, the secret of the very low conductivity of many fibrous and porous materials, and of metal-foil insulation of the Alfol type.

Fluid layers between concentric horizontal or vertical cylinders. Kraussold [4] has shown that if H/H_k, which for cylindrical fluid layers, if H is taken per unit area of inner cylinder, equals $Hd_i\log_e(d_o/d_i)/2k\theta$, is plotted against $\log ag\theta c\delta^3\rho^2/k\mu$, the results, both for liquids and gases, lie on the curve of Fig. 29 provided d_o/d_i is not more than about 5. In this case δ is taken as $(d_o-d_i)/2$. This agreement, however, could not be expected to hold for all sizes, since, at any given value of $(Gr_\delta\,Pr)$ and δ, by making d_o/d_i very big, d_i becomes very small, and it is known that natural convection from a cylinder tends to pure conduction as the diameter becomes very small. Thus, for d_o/d_i approaching infinity, the curve of Fig. 29 for cylindrical layers should be a horizontal straight line, whatever the value of δ, and consequently of $(Gr_\delta\,Pr)$. Experiments extend only to d_o/d_i about 8, but Beckmann [5] made extrapolations for higher values, taking as the limit values calculated from the mean curve for natural convection from a single horizontal cylinder, for which he assumed a d_o/d_i ratio of 100. It should be noted that in this case the full temperature difference between the two surfaces is used

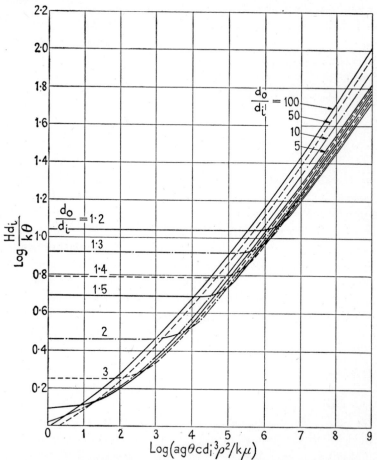

Fig. 30. Natural convection across a layer of fluid between two concentric cylinders of outer and inner diameter d_o and d_i.

when obtaining values from the single cylinder curves, and not one-half the value as in the case of plane surfaces, since, owing to the outer cylinder having so much greater an area than the inner cylinder for $d_o/d_i = 100$, practically the whole of the temperature drop is between inner cylinder and fluid. Fig. 30, in which Nu is plotted against $(Gr_{d_i} Pr)$, with d_i as the characteristic linear dimension, and with θ the temperature difference between the two surfaces, has been derived from Beckmann's curves. At high values of $(Gr_{d_i} Pr)$ a series of parallel curves, each corresponding to a different value of d_o/d_i, is obtained. As $(Gr_{d_i} Pr)$ decreases the curves become horizontal for gradually increasing values of d_o/d_i, and would ultimately become horizontal, showing that the heat transfer is by conduction only, however big d_o/d_i. As d_o/d_i is decreased, Nu decreases for high values of $(Gr_{d_i} Pr)$ and increases for low values.

EXAMPLE 1

A large duct of polished metal (diameter more than 2 ft.) in surroundings at 65° F. carries hot air. If the metal is at 150° F., at what rate per square ft. will the duct lose heat (a) by convection, (b) by convection and radiation together? If the metal were painted white on the outside, what would be the rate of heat loss by convection and radiation together?

Solution. For so large a surface the heat loss by natural convection will be given closely enough by $0.30\theta^{1.25}$ B.Th.U./ft.² hr. irrespective of whether the duct is horizontal or vertical, or partly both (see p. 99). The heat loss will therefore be:

$$0.30 \times (150-65)^{5/4} = 0.30 \times 85^{5/4} = 0.30 \times 258$$
$$= 77 \text{ B.Th.U./ft.}^2 \text{ hr.}$$

Taking the emissivity of the polished surface as 0·10 (see Table XVI), the heat loss by radiation and convection is given by

$$[0.30(150-65)^{5/4} + 1.73 \times 10^{-9} \times 0.10(610^4 - 525^4)]$$
$$= 77 + 11 = 88 \text{ B.Th.U./ft.}^2 \text{ hr.}$$

or, more simply, from Table XVII, by

$$1.04(150-65) = 88 \text{ B.Th.U./ft.}^2 \text{ hr.}$$

For a white-painted surface at 150° F., $E = 0.95$ (see Tables XVI and XVII) the corresponding heat loss by radiation and convection would be

$$2.11(150-65) = 179 \text{ B.Th.U./ft.}^2 \text{ hr.}$$

Actually, it can easily be seen that for air at any given

temperature flowing through a pipe at given velocity, the temperature of the metal when polished on the outside would be higher than when painted and the difference in the heat loss for the two surface conditions would thus be less than that worked out above on the assumption of equal surface temperatures.

EXAMPLE 2

A painted panel 2 ft. square is kept at 140° F. by water circulating through pipes on its reverse surface. Neglecting conduction through the back of the panel, how much heat would it lose (a) when set flush with the ceiling, facing downwards, and (b) when set flush with the floor, facing upwards, in a room at 60° F.?

Solution. (a) Convection for panel

$$= 0.12\theta^{1.25}/l^{0.25} = \frac{0.12 \times (80)^{1.25}}{2^{0.25}}$$

$$= \text{(see Fig. 28)} \frac{0.12 \times 239}{1.19} = 24 \text{ B.Th.U./ft.}^2 \text{ hr.}$$

Radiation $= 1.73 \times 10^{-9} \times 0.9(600^4 - 520^4)$

$$= \text{(see Table XV)} \ 0.9(224 - 126) = 88$$

$$\text{B.Th.U./ft.}^2 \text{ hr.}$$

Convection+radiation $= 24 + 88 = 112$ B.Th.U./ft.^{2} hr.

(b) Since $Gr \ Pr = 8.6 \times 10^8$ (see Table XVIII)

Convection $= 0.35\theta^{1.25} = 0.35 \times 239 = 84$ B.Th.U./ft.^{2} hr.

Radiation, as before, $= 88$ B.Th.U./ft.^{2} hr.

Convection+radiation $= 84 + 88 = 172$ B.Th.U./ft.^{2} hr.

EXAMPLE 3

A bright platinum wire, diameter 0.01 in., is maintained at 1,540° F. in still air at 60° F. Neglecting radiation, at what rate is heat being generated per ft. length of wire?

Solution. Coefficient of expansion, a, $= 1/(460 + 60) = 1/520$. From Table XVIII, for air at mean temperature, t_m, 800° F.,

$$gc\rho^2/k\mu = 4.48 \times 10^7, \quad \text{and} \quad k = 0.0286 \text{ B.Th.U./ft. hr. °F.}$$

Temperature difference, θ, from wire to air $= 1,480$ degs. F.
Wire diameter $= 1/1200$ ft.

Hence

$$(Gr \ Pr) = \frac{ag\theta c\rho^2 d^3}{k\mu} = (4{\cdot}48 \times 10^7 \times 1480)/(520 \times 1200^3)$$

and $\log(Gr \ Pr) = -1{\cdot}3.$

Hence, from Fig. 24,

$$\log Nu = -0{\cdot}13 = \bar{1}{\cdot}87 = \log 0{\cdot}74,$$

and $Hd/k\theta = 0{\cdot}74.$

Heat production per foot length of wire $= \pi dH = 0{\cdot}74 \times \pi \times k\theta$

$$= 0{\cdot}74 \times 3{\cdot}14 \times 0{\cdot}0286 \times 1480 = 98 \text{ B.Th.U./hr.}$$

If, instead of the temperature of the wire, the heat input were given, and the temperature attained by the wire required, a preliminary guess would have to be made.

Suppose a wire temperature of 1,140° F. were taken, giving $\theta = 1,080$ F.$^{\circ}$ and t_m 600° F. Then:

$$(Gr \ Pr) = (8{\cdot}0 \times 10^7 \times 1080)/(520 \times 1200^3)$$

whence $\log(Gr \ Pr) = 1{\cdot}02$

and, from Fig. 24,

$$\log Nu = -0{\cdot}11 = \bar{1}{\cdot}89 = \log 0{\cdot}78.$$

Heat loss per foot length $= \pi Hd = \pi \times 0{\cdot}78 k\theta$

$$= 3{\cdot}14 \times 0{\cdot}78 \times 0{\cdot}025 \times 1080$$

$$= 66 \text{ B.Th.U./hr.}$$

This is too small, so evidently the wire temperature has been guessed too low. Inspection of Fig. 24 shows that, in the region of the curve involved, the slope is about $0{\cdot}15$, indicating that H is nearly proportional to $\theta^{1{\cdot}15}$.

Hence the true temperature difference θ should be nearly given by

$$(\theta/1080)^{1{\cdot}15} = 98/66$$

$$1{\cdot}15 \log(\theta/1080) = \log(98/66) = 0{\cdot}173$$

$$\log \theta = 0{\cdot}15 + 3{\cdot}033 = 3{\cdot}183$$

$$= \log 1520.$$

This gives a wire temperature of 1,580° F. which is much nearer the correct one, and, considering the scatter of the experimental points, about as good an estimate as the data are capable of providing. It is, in fact, within 5 per cent. of the actual temperature.

BIBLIOGRAPHY

NATURAL CONVECTION

1. SAUNDERS, O. A. 'The Effect of Pressure upon Natural Convection in Air.' *Proc. Roy. Soc.* A, 1936, **157**, 278. Also 'Natural Convection in Liquids'. *Proc. Roy. Soc.* A, 1939, **172**, 55.

2. TOULOUKIAN, Y. S., HAWKINS, G. A., and JAKOB, M. 'Heat Transfer by Free Convection from Heated Vertical Surfaces to Liquids.' *Trans. Am. Soc. Mech. Eng.* 1948, **70**, 13.

3. JAKOB, M. 'Free Heat Conduction through Enclosed Plane Gas Layers.' *Trans. Am. Soc. Mech. Eng.* 1946, **68**, 189.

4. KRAUSSOLD, H. 'Wärmeabgabe von cylindrischen Flüssigkeiten bei naturlicher Konvektion.' *Forsch. Gebiete Ingenieurwes.* 1934, **5**, 186.

5. BECKMANN, W. 'Die Wärmeübertragung in zylindrischen Gasschichten bei naturlicher Konvektion.' *Forsch. Gebiete Ingenieurwes.* 1931, **2**, 165.

VI

FORCED CONVECTION

FORCED convection, as has already been explained in Chapter III, occurs when a fluid is in contact with a surface at a different temperature, the motion being due to pressures or velocities applied to the fluid, independently of the heat flow. Strictly speaking, natural convection effects are never entirely absent, but at high enough speeds of forced flow they can be neglected.

Heat transfer by forced convection has been investigated more or less systematically for flow through and across pipes and flow over plane surfaces. Of these, the most important industrially are flow through pipes and flow over 'banks', or 'nests', of parallel pipes. With forced convection, since the flow requires power to maintain it, heat transfer must be considered in relation to pressure drop, the power available often being limited. Usually questions of the weight or size of plant also arise and a compromise is necessary in choosing design conditions.

TURBULENT FLOW OF FLUIDS THROUGH PIPES

A great many measurements have been made of the heat transfer between the inner surfaces of pipes and gases or liquids flowing through them in turbulent flow. The gases include air, carbon dioxide, coal gas, combustion gases, hydrogen-nitrogen mixtures, and superheated steam. The experiments on superheated steam, oxygen, air, and hydrogen-nitrogen mixtures went up to pressures of about 9, 11, 14, and 900 atmospheres respectively. For the other gases the experiments were carried out at atmospheric pressure. The liquids used include water, acetone, benzene, kerosene, and various oils and alcohols. Pipe diameters, d, ranged from $\frac{1}{2}$ in. to nearly 6 in., and temperature differences, θ, from a few degrees to 2,000 F.° For both gases and liquids the experimental range of Reynolds number extends to about 5×10^5.

It has been found, as shown in Fig. 31, that the data correlate fairly well by plotting $\log(Nu/Pr^{0.4})$ against $\log Re$. Strictly, for similarity, the ratio of pipe diameter to pipe length, d/l, should be included, or the results plotted for only one value of d/l at a time; but comparison of results for different values shows that the power of d/l involved is only about 0·05, so that for ratios of l to d above about 10 it can for practical purposes be neglected. In Fig. 31 the rings represent data for liquids, while the straight

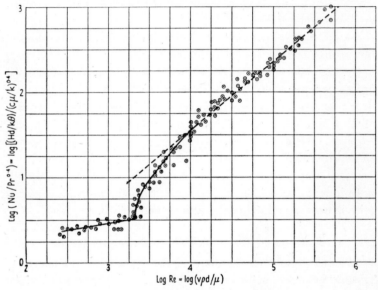

FIG. 31. Forced convection for fluids flowing through pipes. ⊙s are experimental points for liquids. Dotted line is mean curve for gases.

line is the mean through the data for gases, the equation to which is

$$Nu = 0·023 Re^{0·8} Pr^{0·4}. \tag{53}$$

It will be seen that for gases this relation holds down to the critical value of $Re = 2100$ ($\log Re = 3·3$); but it must be remembered that the majority of experiments were for pipe diameters of, at the most, an inch or two, and there is some evidence that for very low rates of flow in wider pipes natural convection currents may become appreciable, and divergencies from (53) consequently occur even for Re above 2100. In such cases the heat transfer might be expected to vary with the inclination of the pipe. For liquids the slope of the curve gradually increases as Re decreases from 5000 to 2100 (i.e. as $\log Re$ decreases from 3·7 to 3·3), this being the transition region between full turbulence and streamline flow. At $Re = 2100$ there is a sudden sharp decrease in the slope of the curve, which is now in the streamline region of Re. These non-turbulent regions will, in the case of liquids, be discussed more fully later, but the data have been included on the curve for turbulent flow in Fig. 31 to give a general picture over the whole range of Re, from streamline to fully turbulent.

The gas data could, of course, have been plotted in terms of Nu only, since Pr varies very little either from gas to gas, or with temperature for any given gas. But it is convenient for comparison to plot both gases and liquids in the same way. Substituting for the Pr term, however, the equation to the dotted straight line curve for gases becomes:

$$Nu = 0 \cdot 020 Re^{0 \cdot 8}. \tag{54}$$

In calculating Nu, Pr, and Re for the points plotted in Fig. 31 the physical constants k, μ, and c were taken at the mean bulk temperature of the fluid, i.e. at the mean of the inlet and outlet mixing temperatures. At what temperature v and ρ are taken makes no difference, so long as they are both taken at the same temperature, since $v\rho$ is constant along a pipe, and equal to M, the mass velocity, or mass rate of flow per unit area of pipe cross-section.

If the temperature differences, θ_1 and θ_2, between fluid and pipe wall at the beginning and end of the section considered are very different, the logarithmic mean temperature difference, which is given by $(\theta_1-\theta_2)/\log_e(\theta_1/\theta_2)$, must be taken when calculating the heat transfer for the whole section, i.e. the heat transfer along the section must be integrated. If θ_1 and θ_2 do not differ much, their arithmetic mean may be taken without much error. The ratio of the logarithmic to the arithmetic mean temperature difference depends upon the ratio of θ_1 to θ_2, as is shown in Fig. 32, from which it will be seen that as θ_1/θ_2 increases from 1 to 20 the ratio of the log mean to the arithmetic mean temperature difference decreases from 1·0 to 0·6. For θ_1/θ_2 below 3, less than 10 per cent. error is introduced by taking the arithmetic mean for θ, which is within the accuracy of the experimental data.

Making use of the fact that, for gases, $c\mu/k$ is nearly constant at about 0·75, expression (54) can be written in several alternative

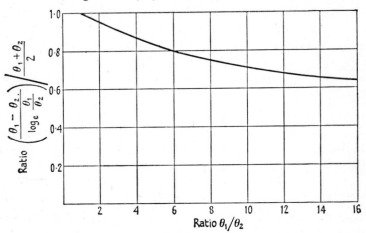

Fig. 32. Relation between logarithmic and arithmetic mean temperature difference.

forms. For instance the viscosity term can be eliminated by substituting $0·75k/c$ for μ, giving

$$Nu = 0·026(v\rho dc/k)^{0·8} = 0·026(Re\ Pr)^{0·8}. \qquad (55)$$

The dimensionless group $v\rho dc/k$, which is the product of Re and Pr, is known as the Péclet number, $Pé$, and has been used by several investigators for calculating heat transfer data for gases.

Similarly k can be eliminated from (54) by substituting for it $c\mu/0·75$, giving

$$H/\theta = \alpha = 0·027c(v\rho)^{0·8}(\mu/d)^{0·2}\ \text{B.Th.U./ft.}^2\ \text{hr. }°\text{F.} \qquad (56)$$

Variation of heat transfer coefficient with temperature.
It can be seen from (53) that for any given pipe diameter and any given mass velocity, $v\rho$, α varies with temperature in proportion to the variation of $(k/\mu^{0·8})(c\mu/k)^{0·4}$, or, for gases, of $k/\mu^{0·8}$. For gases k and μ both increase with increasing temperature and the rate of variation of $k/\mu^{0·8}$ is comparatively slow. For air, as shown in the

correction curve to Fig. 33, α increases by 24, 43, and 50 per cent. as the temperature at which k and μ are taken increases from 60° F. to 1,000° F., 2,000° F., and 3,000° F. respectively. Unfortunately this variation cannot be confirmed directly, since flue gases have been used for high temperature work, and there is then an uncertain correction for gas radiation, of the same order as the temperature correction.

Variation of heat transfer coefficient with gas velocity and pipe diameter. Since $Hd/k\theta$ is proportional to $(v\rho d/\mu)^{0.8}$, if the variation of $k/\mu^{0.8}$ is neglected, H/θ becomes proportional to $(v\rho)^{0.8}/d^{0.2}$ and H_l/θ, the heat transfer coefficient per unit length of pipe, proportional to $(v\rho d)^{0.8}$.

Total length and total weight of tubing necessary for a fixed total mass flow and a fixed change in fluid temperature between inlet and outlet. Suppose n tubes each of diameter d and length l are arranged in parallel. If the total mass flow is fixed, $nd^2v = $ constant, where v is the velocity. If also the change in fluid temperature from inlet to outlet is fixed, the total rate of heat transfer is fixed, that is $nl(vd)^{0.8} = $ constant. Eliminating v from these two equations it follows that

$$nl/(nd)^{0.8} = \text{constant.}$$

Hence the total length of tubing required, nl, is proportional to $(nd)^{0.8}$, showing that if either the number of pipes or their diameter be reduced in any ratio x, the total length needed is reduced in the ratio $x^{0.8}$. For constant pipe-wall thickness the total weight of metal tubing is proportional to nld, that is to $n^{0.8}d^{1.8}$, showing that the weight decreases in the ratio $x^{0.8}$ when the number is reduced in ratio x, and in the ratio $x^{1.8}$ when the diameter is reduced in ratio x.

The length of the individual pipe, l, varies as $d^{0.8}/n^{0.2}$ and is therefore smaller using smaller diameters, but slightly bigger if smaller numbers are used. The overall shape of the pipe nest, which, for spacing between pipes proportional to d, may be expressed by the ratio of the individual pipe length to the nest diameter, $l/d\sqrt{n}$, varies as $1/(n^{0.7}d^{0.2})$, showing that if the aim were for minimum total weight or volume, disregarding pressure drop, it would be best to use a few long pipes of small diameter, through which the fluid moved with high velocity, but the resulting nest might then become inconveniently long and narrow.

Pressure drop, fan power, and ratio of fan work to total heat transferred. The previous section ignores considerations of pressure drop and fan power. Suppose that the total mass flow rate and total heat transfer rate are constant as before. For turbulence, the pressure drop may be taken as approximately proportional to lv^2/d (see p. 79). For fixed mass flow nd^2v is constant, and for fixed heat transfer $nl(vd)^{0.8}$ is constant. It follows that the pressure drop varies as $1/(n^{2.2}d^{4.2})$. The fan work per unit time is given by the pressure drop multiplied by the volume flow rate, and since the latter is fixed the fan power also is proportional to $1/(n^{2.2}d^{4.2})$, or the ratio of total heat transferred to fan work proportional to $n^{2.2}d^{4.2}$. It should be noted, however, that in practice n and d are not independent, being governed largely by design considerations of size, weight, shape, etc. If, for instance, the design requirements were such that the total volume of the bank were fixed, so that nd^2l was constant, it would follow that $nd^{3.5} = $ constant, and $n^{2.2}d^{4.2}$ proportional to $1/d^{3.5}$ or to n. In such a case the ratio of heat transfer to fan power would be best for a large number of short pipes of small diameter. There would, however, usually be practical limits to the reduction in d feasible, since in the extreme the bank would become very short, with large frontal area, so that its inconvenient shape might put it out of question.

Other cases can be worked out in a similar manner. For instance, if a bank were of fixed cross-section, the ratio of heat transfer to pressure drop would be proportional to $1/d^{0.2}$.

Variation of heat transfer coefficient with pressure. Very few measurements of k and μ have been made for gases at high pressures, and these show serious discrepancies, although they agree in suggesting that both properties increase with pressure. It can, however, be deduced from indirect evidence that, until the critical point is approached, the effect of pressure upon the heat transfer is relatively small, except in so far as it affects ρ, and therefore the mass flow. Thus, provided the correct

mass velocity is taken, comparatively little error would be introduced by taking k and μ both at atmospheric pressure [1].

Simplified presentation of heat transfer coefficients.
The heat transfer coefficients for different rates of air flow, and

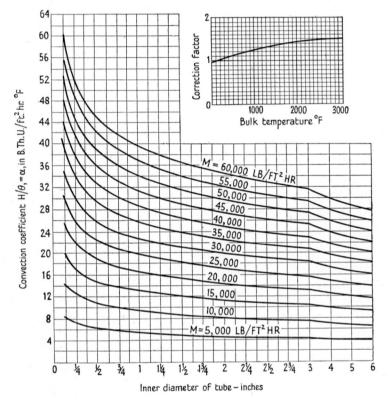

FIG. 33. Heat transfer coefficients for different weights of air per unit area of
pipe cross-section per unit time flowing through pipes of different diameters,
with k and μ taken at 60° F.

different pipe diameters, can be read directly from Figs. 33 and
34, which are based on expression (54) for turbulent flow with
k and μ taken at 60° F. In Fig. 33 the curves are for different
mass velocities, i.e. mass rates of flow per unit area of pipe cross-
section; in Fig. 34 they are for different linear velocities measured
at 60° F. and 1 atmosphere. It should be noted that, for the
lower velocities and smaller pipe diameters, the flow may not be

turbulent, and the curves therefore not applicable, except for low temperatures, at which the gas viscosity is relatively low.

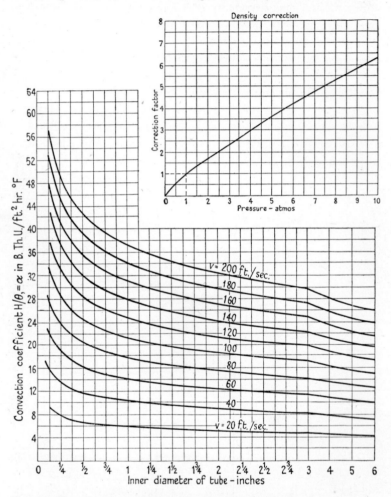

FIG. 34. Heat transfer coefficients for air at 60° F. flowing through pipes of different diameters at different velocities.

A correction curve is given which shows the factors by which the heat transfer coefficients should be multiplied when the air temperature is above 60° F., and in the case of Fig. 34, when the pressure is above 1 atmosphere. No pressure correction is required for Fig. 33, which, since the flow is given in lb./ft.^{2} hr., automatically takes account of changes of ρ due to changes of pressure. Fig. 33 is applicable with no significant error to carbon monoxide, nitrogen, and oxygen for which k and μ are nearly the same as for air. For carbon dioxide at 100° F. the heat transfer for any given mass velocity and pipe diameter is only about three-quarters that for air, but becomes equal to that for air at about 800° F.; for higher temperatures it is slightly greater than that for air.

Hydrogen gives exceptionally high heat transfer because it has a high thermal conductivity and low viscosity. For the same mass velocity the coefficient for temperatures around 100° F. to 200° F. is thirteen times, for higher temperatures twelve times, that for air.

The heat transfer for methane is also high, although not nearly so high as for hydrogen; it varies from about twice that for air at 100° F. to nearly $3\frac{1}{2}$ times at 2,000° F. For ethane the corresponding factors are $1\frac{1}{2}$ and 3; for ethylene 1·3 and 2·5.

For superheated steam at atmospheric pressure there is some uncertainty about the values of k at the higher temperatures, but for the same mass velocity, the heat transfer according to (53) is, between 300° F. and 800° F., about 1·5 times that for air, rising to about twice that for air at 2,000° F.

For high-pressure steam neither k nor μ is known with any accuracy, but it seems that, for the same mass velocity, the ratios to air are much the same as at atmospheric pressure up to 250 lb./sq. in., but for higher pressures, especially at the lower temperatures near the critical point, the heat transfer in relation to that for air becomes much greater. For instance, at 1,500 lb./sq. in. and 600° F. it is about three times that for air.

Heat transfer for liquids flowing through pipes. In comparing the rates of heat transfer for different liquids the variation of the Pr term in (53) must be taken into account, and it can be seen that the heat transfer for any given mass velocity and tube diameter depends upon $(k/\mu^{0\cdot8})(c\mu/k)^{0\cdot4}$, i.e. upon $(k^{0\cdot6}c^{0\cdot4})/\mu^{0\cdot4}$. Coefficients for water are given in Figs. 35 and 36 for mass and linear velocities respectively again with k and μ

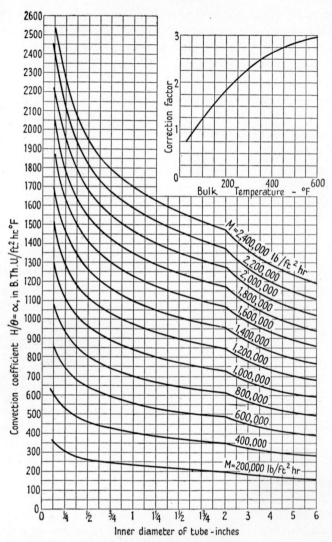

FIG. 35. Heat transfer coefficients for different weights of water per unit area of pipe cross-section per unit time flowing through pipes of different diameters, with k and μ taken at 60° F.

taken at 60° F. A subsidiary correction curve for fluid temperatures above 60° F. is given. This is applicable to both figures, provided the linear velocities are reduced to 60° F., before

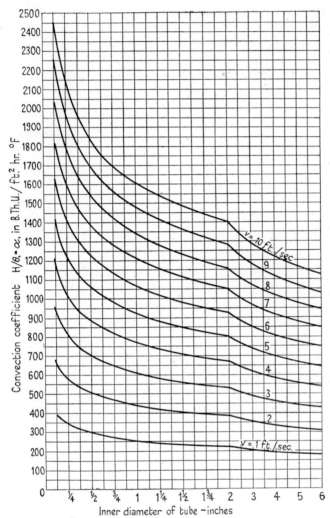

Fig. 36. Heat transfer coefficients for water at 60° F. flowing through pipes of different diameter at different velocities.

reading values from Fig. 36. Water has a higher thermal conductivity, and higher specific heat, than any other non-metallic liquid; it thus gives a relatively high rate of heat transfer. For liquids μ usually decreases quickly, and k decreases slowly, with increasing temperature, while c increases. The net effect is an increase in H/θ with increasing temperature. For water the increase in H/θ is 85, 165, 295 per cent. as the temperature increases from 60° F. to 200° F., 400° F., 600° F. respectively.

Comparing Figs. 35 and 36 with the corresponding Figs. 33 and 34 for air, it will be seen that for the same mass velocity the heat transfer coefficients for water are about $2\frac{1}{4}$ times those for air. For the same linear velocity the heat transfer coefficients for water are at 60° F. about 500 times, and at 200° F. about 1,000 times, those for air.

Some liquids, mainly because of their very high viscosity, but also because they have relatively low thermal conductivity and specific heat, give, in turbulent flow, very much lower heat transfer coefficients than water for the same mass velocity. Thus glycerol, even in turbulent flow, would at 60° F. give only about one-twentieth, and many other liquids only one-half to one-third the heat transfer of water. It must, however, be remembered that for the more viscous liquids the motion is often laminar, when (53) no longer applies.

Effect of direction of temperature gradient. Actually, for liquids flowing through pipes, even when turbulent, the heat transfer coefficients depend to some extent upon whether the pipe is the hotter, and the liquid consequently being warmed, or the pipe the colder, and the liquid consequently being cooled. This is because of the variation of viscosity with temperature, which, when the pipe is hot, causes the viscosity μ_s of the liquid in contact with it to be lower, and when the pipe is cold to be higher, than the viscosity μ in the main stream. (53) may, however, be used without serious error either for warming or cooling except for liquids of high viscosity, for which closer results are given by

$$Nu = 0.027(\mu/\mu_s)^{0.14} Re^{0.8} Pr^{0.33}. \tag{57}$$

Streamline Flow of Fluids through Pipes

When a fluid is in streamline flow through a pipe at a different temperature, the velocity distribution, which for isothermal flow is parabolic (see p. 78), will be distorted in a way depending upon whether the pipe is hotter or cooler than the fluid, and whether the fluid is a liquid or a gas. For liquids, viscosity decreases with increasing temperature, and the velocity near the pipe wall will, for the same main stream velocity, be higher than that for isothermal flow when the pipe is the hotter; when the pipe is the colder, the velocity near it will be lower than that for isothermal flow.

For gases, viscosity increases with increasing temperature, and these effects are reversed.

Theoretical expressions for the heat transfer, which for pure streamline flow can take place only by radial conduction, have been worked out on the assumption of parabolic velocity distribution, but these would not be expected to apply accurately for large temperature differences, or for fluids whose physical properties, particularly viscosity, vary rapidly with temperature.

Theoretically Nu is related to $(Re \times Pr \times d/l)$ by a complicated expression involving infinite series. The theory, as developed by Graetz [2], Nusselt [3], Lévêque [4], and others, indicates that the local heat transfer coefficient should be infinite at the pipe inlet, decreasing with distance l along the pipe, until ultimately, when l is large enough for $(Re \times Pr \times d/l)$ to be less than about 17, it becomes constant, and equal to $3 \cdot 65k/d$ or $5 \cdot 15k/d$, according to whether the temperature difference from pipe surface to fluid is based on the mean mixing temperature of the fluid, i.e. the mean temperature weighted according to the velocity, or on the unweighted mean temperature. For the special case in which the temperature along the pipe surface varies in such a way that the temperature difference between pipe and fluid remains constant the corresponding expressions become $4 \cdot 36k/d$ and $6 \cdot 0k/d$.

For shorter lengths corresponding to values of $(Re \times Pr \times d/l)$ above about 12, the theoretical curve for the mean heat transfer coefficient over the entire pipe length is expressed nearly by

$$Nu = 1 \cdot 62\left[(Re\ Pr)\left(\frac{d}{l}\right)\right]^{\frac{1}{3}} = 1 \cdot 62\left(\frac{4wc}{\pi kl}\right)^{\frac{1}{3}} = 1 \cdot 75\left(\frac{wc}{kl}\right)^{\frac{1}{3}}. \quad (58)$$

In the above expression the temperature difference to be taken is $[(t_s - t_1) + (t_s - t_2)]/2$, where t_s is the tube temperature, assumed uniform, t_1 the inlet, and t_2 the mean mixing outlet temperature, and $w, = (\pi/4) \times v\rho d^2$, is the mass flow in lb./hr. The dimensionless group wc/kl is known as the Graetz number.

For the special case of a pipe so long that the fluid has nearly reached the wall temperature, that is $t_s = t_2$,

$$[(t_s - t_1) + (t_s - t_2)]/2 = (t_2 - t_1)/2,$$

and by equating the heat gained by the liquid to the heat transfer from the pipe,

$$wc(t_2 - t_1) = [\pi dl \times (H/\theta) \times (t_2 - t_1)]/2,$$

or $\qquad \dfrac{H}{\theta} = \dfrac{2wc}{\pi dl} \quad$ and $\quad Nu = \dfrac{Hd}{k\theta} = \dfrac{2wc}{\pi kl}.$ $\qquad$ (59)

Experiments with viscous liquids give results respectively above or below those indicated by (58), according to whether the liquid is flowing through a hotter or colder pipe. Sieder and Tate [5], however, have shown that the results for heating and cooling can be brought into agreement by including a term $(\mu/\mu_s)^{0\cdot14}$, their equation being

$$Nu = 1 \cdot 86 (\mu/\mu_s)^{0\cdot14} [(Re\ Pr)(d/l)]^{\frac{1}{3}} = 2 \cdot 01 \left(\frac{wc}{kl}\right)^{\frac{1}{3}} \left(\frac{\mu}{\mu_s}\right)^{0\cdot14}. \quad (60)$$

This is the equation which should be used for the heating or cooling of viscous fluids flowing through pipes at Re less than 2,100, when wc/kl is greater than 10. It is based on a range of d from 0·4 in. to 1·6 in., of l from 3 ft. to nearly 12 ft., and of μ/μ_s from 0·004 to 14. When wc/kl is less than 10, t_2 becomes nearly equal to t_s, and (59) applies. As θ approaches zero, (μ/μ_s), and consequently also $(\mu/\mu_s)^{0\cdot14}$, approaches unity, and (60) would be expected to reduce to (58). Actually the two differ in the constants, 1·86 and 1·62. It may be that in some of the experiments the flow was not truly streamline, and the velocity distribution not quite parabolic. According to Boussinesq's [6] theory, even for isothermal flow at Re below 2,100, the parabolic distribution is not established until a minimum distance l along the pipe is reached, given by $l/d = 0\cdot065Re$, so for $Re = 2,000$, $l/d = 130$, or for $Re = 1,000$, $l/d = 65$.

Effect of natural convection. As already mentioned on p. 69, for forced convection at low Re the buoyancy forces due to differences in temperature may be appreciable in comparison with the forces independent of temperature. It may then be no longer permissible to neglect Gr (i.e. $ag\theta d^3\rho^2/\mu^2$). Colburn [7] found that data for air, water, and petroleum oil were well expressed by

Grashof

$$Nu = Hd/k\theta = 1\cdot62\left[\left(\frac{\mu}{\mu_f}\right)^{\frac{1}{3}}(1+0\cdot015Gr^{\frac{1}{3}})\right]\left(\frac{4wc}{\pi kl}\right)^{\frac{1}{3}}, \quad (61)$$

where H/θ in Nu is the mean heat transfer coefficient based on a temperature difference calculated as for (58). Several observers, however, have found that the results given by (61) tend to be low.

Since for viscous liquids in tubes of ordinary diameter Gr is small, expression (60) can safely be used even for low values of Re, except in very unusual cases.

Transition between turbulence and streamline flow. By comparing (53) and (60) it is seen that for $Re > 10,000$, Nu, for liquids, is proportional to $Re^{0\cdot8}$ and independent of d/l, while for $Re < 2,100$ it is proportional to $Re^{0\cdot33}$ and to $(d/l)^{0\cdot33}$. Hence, in the transition range, as Re decreases below $10,000$, Nu will depend upon a power of Re progressively decreasing from $0\cdot8$ to $0\cdot33$, and upon a power of d/l progressively increasing from 0 to $0\cdot33$. For gases, or for liquids of low viscosity, the results in this range of Re may be modified by natural convection effects. A number of experiments have been carried out, mainly for viscous liquids, and for more detailed results the reader is referred to McAdams's *Heat Transmission*.

NON-CIRCULAR PIPES

Cope [8] found that the heat transfer coefficients for water flowing through pipes of section varying from $\frac{1}{2}$ in. square to 1 in. $\times\frac{1}{8}$ in. agreed well with values calculated from the circular pipe formula (53), provided that, in calculating Nu and Re, the hydraulic diameter of the non-circular pipe (i.e. $4\times$ cross-sectional area/perimeter) were taken. For any given value of Re, the friction factor for the very flat pipe was appreciably above that for the others. Washington and Marks [9], with air flowing through heated rectangular passages of cross-section 5 in. by $\frac{1}{8}$ in., $\frac{1}{4}$ in., and $\frac{9}{16}$ in. respectively, found that for Re above 13,000 the Nu-Re curves, if based on mean hydraulic diameter, followed those for circular pipes. For the lower values of Re the results for the wider ducts still agreed with those for circular pipes, but the heat transfer for the most elongated section was considerably below that for circular pipes. This was believed to be due to a damping of the free convection currents as the walls were brought closer together.

Calculation of Outlet Temperature of Fluid flowing through a Pipe

If the temperature, t_1, of a fluid at one cross-section of a pipe is known, and it is required to find the temperature, t_2, at a cross-section l ft. farther along the pipe, an approximate heat transfer coefficient, α, must first be worked out with the physical constants involved based on either the temperature, t_1, or on a mean fluid temperature deduced from a guessed value of t_2. By equating the heat transfer for the length l, given by

$$\alpha\left(t - \frac{t_1 + t_2}{2}\right) \times \pi dl,$$

where t is the temperature of the pipe, assumed uniform, to the heat gained or lost by the fluid, given by $Mc \times \dfrac{\pi d^2}{4}(t_2 - t_1)$, where M is the mass velocity, an approximate value for t_2 can be found. For turbulent flow of a gas through a pipe, α, for given values of M and d, is proportional to $k/\mu^{0\cdot 8}$, which changes only slowly with changing temperature. In this case the initial result is often near enough. But if the calculated value of t_2 indicates that the values of the physical constants used in finding α need appreciable modification, a second and more accurate calculation must be made with the physical constants taken at a more correct temperature, i.e. at the mean of t_1 and t_2 (calculated). The value of t_2 must then be recalculated on the basis of the new α. The process can be repeated if necessary.

EXAMPLE 1

A pipe of inside diameter $\frac{1}{2}$ in. is kept at 400° F. Air flows through it at 10 lb./hr. What length of pipe is needed to warm the air from 50° F. to 250° F.?

Solution. From Table XVIII, for air at $(50+250)/2 = 150°$ F., viscosity, μ, $= 0\cdot049$ lb./ft. hr., thermal conductivity, k, $= 0\cdot0164$ B.Th.U./ft. hr. °F., and specific heat, c, $= 0\cdot24$ B.Th.U./lb. °F.

Mass velocity, M, per unit cross-section, $= 10/\pi r^2$ lb./ft.² hr. Hence

$$Re = Md/\mu = (10 \times 2r)/\pi r^2 \mu = (20 \times 48)/0\cdot049\pi = 6\cdot23 \times 10^3.$$

The flow will thus be turbulent, and the heat transfer given by (54), $Nu = Hd/k\theta = 0\cdot020 Re^{0\cdot8} = 0\cdot020 \times 1\cdot085 \times 10^3 = 21\cdot7.$

The heat transfer for length $l = 21\cdot7 \times k\theta \times (\pi dl/d)$

$$= 21\cdot7 \times 0\cdot0164 \times 250 \times 3\cdot14l = 280l \text{ B.Th.U./hr.}$$

Heat required to warm air 200 F.° $= 200 \times 10 \times 0\cdot24$

$$= 480 \text{ B.Th.U./hr.}$$

Hence $280l = 480$, and $l = 12/7 = 1\cdot71$ ft.

EXAMPLE 2

With the same conditions as in Example 1 what mass of air per hour, w, would be warmed from 50° F. to 250° F. in a 1·71 ft. length of pipe, assuming turbulent flow?

Solution. $Hd/k\theta = 0\cdot020(6\cdot23 \times 10^2)^{0\cdot8}w^{0\cdot8}$, and heat transfer for length 1·71 ft. $= 280 \times 1\cdot71 \times (w/10)^{0\cdot8}$ B.Th.U./hr.

Heat required to warm air $= 200 \times 0\cdot24 \times w = 48w$ B.Th.U./hr.

Hence $w^{0\cdot2} = (280 \times 1\cdot71)/(6\cdot31 \times 48) = 1\cdot58$, and $w = 10$ lb./hr.

EXAMPLE 3

Suppose in Example 1 only the inlet air temperature, 50° F., had been given, and the problem were to determine the outlet temperature, t, at a distance 1·71 ft. along the pipe.

Solution. In this case, since t is not known, a rough guess at its value must be made for the purpose of finding the mean air temperature, t_m, at which to take k and μ.

Suppose a bad guess of 150° F. is made, so that
$$t_m = (50+150)/2 = 100° \text{ F.}$$

From Table XVIII,
$$k = 0 \cdot 0154 \text{ B.Th.U./ft. hr. °F.}, \quad \mu = 0 \cdot 046 \text{ lb./ft. hr.}$$

The new Re, which is different only in so far as μ is different, will be $6 \cdot 2 \times 10^3 \times (49/46) = 6 \cdot 7 \times 10^3$, whence
$$Re^{0 \cdot 8} = 1 \cdot 15 \times 10^3 \quad \text{and} \quad Hd/k\theta = 23 \cdot 0, \quad \text{and} \quad H/\theta = 23k/d.$$

Then
$$\frac{23 \times 0 \cdot 0154 \times \pi d}{d} \times 1 \cdot 71 \times \left(400 - \frac{50+t}{2}\right) = 10 \times 0 \cdot 24(t-50),$$

whence $(750-t) = 2 \cdot 52(t-50)$ and $t = 249°$ F.

The effect of taking k and μ at 100° F. instead of at 150° F. is thus seen to be negligible.

Example 4

What length of pipe, internal diameter 1 in., maintained at 200° F., is required to warm water flowing through it at 2,000 lb./hr. from 50° F. to 100° F.?

Solution. From Table XVIII, for water at 75° F.,
$$\mu = 2 \cdot 24 \text{ lb./ft. hr.}, \quad k = 0 \cdot 35 \text{ B.Th.U./ft. hr. °F.},$$
$$Pr = 6 \cdot 4, \quad \text{and} \quad c = 1 \cdot 00 \text{ B.Th.U./lb. °F.}$$

Hence $Re = (2000 \times 48)/(\pi \times 2 \cdot 24) = 1 \cdot 36 \times 10^4$ and (53) may be used.
$$Re^{0 \cdot 8} = 2 \cdot 03 \times 10^3, \quad \text{and} \quad Pr^{0 \cdot 4} = 2 \cdot 10.$$

Hence $Hd/k\theta = 0 \cdot 023 Re^{0 \cdot 8} Pr^{0 \cdot 4} = 98$.

Heat transfer for length l
$$= 98 \times 0 \cdot 35 \times 125 \times \pi l = 10 \cdot 8 \times 10^3 \times l.$$

Heat required to warm water $= 2000 \times 50 = 10^5$ B.Th.U./hr.

Hence $l = 10^5/(1 \cdot 08 \times 10^4) = 9 \cdot 3$ ft.

Example 5

In the above problem, what is the value of the heat transfer coefficient?

Solution. The heat transfer coefficient
$$H/\theta = (k/d) \times 0 \cdot 023 Re^{0 \cdot 8} Pr^{0 \cdot 4}$$
$$= 0 \cdot 35 \times 12 \times 98 = 412 \text{ B.Th.U./ft.}^2 \text{ hr. °F.}$$

Alternatively the heat transfer coefficient for a mass flow per unit area of pipe cross-section $= 2000/\pi r^2 = 366000$ lb./ft.^{2} hr. could have been estimated directly from Fig. 35, giving a value of about 385 B.Th.U./ft.^{2} hr. °F. for μ and k at 60° F., which needs multiplying by about 1·07 (see subsidiary curve on Fig. 35) for μ and k at 75° F., giving a corrected value practically the same as the calculated, i.e. 412 B.Th.U./ft.^{2} hr. °F.

EXAMPLE 6

A thermocouple of diameter $\frac{1}{25}$ in. and emissivity 0·5 is normal to an air stream flowing at 10 ft./sec. through a wide duct with inner walls at 1,200° F. If the thermocouple indicates an air temperature of 1,400° F., what is the true value? For calculating convection between the thermocouple and the air take

$$Nu = 0 \cdot 8Re^{0 \cdot 38}$$

with the diameter of the thermocouple as the characteristic linear dimension, and with k and μ taken at the mean film temperature.

What would be the approximate reading of the thermocouple if the air velocity were doubled, other things remaining the same?

Solution. The thermocouple will take up an equilibrium temperature such that the heat it gains from the air by convection is equal to the heat it loses to the walls by radiation. Evidently the true gas temperature, t, is above 1,400° F. As a guess, taking k and μ at 1,450° F. from Table XVIII, and assuming the true gas temperature to be about 1,500° F. so that $\rho = 0 \cdot 020$ lb./ft.^{3},

$$Re = \frac{10 \times 60 \times 60 \times 0 \cdot 020}{25 \times 12 \times 0 \cdot 10} = 24.$$

Hence $Hd/k\theta = 0 \cdot 8 \times 24^{0 \cdot 38} = 2 \cdot 68,$

and $H/\theta = 0 \cdot 039 \times 25 \times 12 \times 2 \cdot 68 = 31 \cdot 5 \dfrac{\text{B.Th.U.}}{\text{ft.}^2 \text{ hr. °F.}}.$

Since the wire is small compared with its surroundings the emissivity of the surroundings can be taken as unity in calculating the radiation from thermocouple to duct walls, and expression (5) used.

Hence $31 \cdot 5(t-1400) = 1 \cdot 73 \times 10^{-9} \times 0 \cdot 5(1860^4 - 1660^4)$

$$= 0 \cdot 5(20800 - 13100) \text{ (see Table XV).}$$

Whence $t = 1400 + \dfrac{0 \cdot 5 \times 7700}{31 \cdot 5} = 1,522° $ F., which is so near the preliminary guess of 1,500° F. that the temperatures at which k, μ, and ρ have been taken are evidently near enough to involve no significant error.

If the velocity were doubled the coefficient of convection would become approximately

$$31{\cdot}5 \times 2^{0{\cdot}38} = 41 \text{ B.Th.U./ft.}^2 \text{ hr. }°\text{F.},$$

so, if t' is the temperature of the thermocouple,

$$41(1522-t') = 1{\cdot}73 \times 10^{-9} \times 0{\cdot}5[(t'+460)^4 - 1660^4],$$

from which, by a process of trial and error, it will be found that $t' = 1,419°$ F.

EXAMPLE 7

Oil at 140° F. enters a pipe of inner diameter $\frac{1}{4}$ in. maintained uniformly at 80° F. Taking the viscosity of the oil as 5 centipoises, its specific gravity as 0·9, specific heat as 0·5 B.Th.U./lb. °F., and thermal conductivity as 0·80 B.Th.U./ft. hr. °F., what length of pipe would be required to cool 10 gals. per hour to 110° F.?

Solution. From p. 200, 1 centipoise = 2·42 lb./ft. hr.

Hence

$$Re = \frac{10 \times 10 \times 0{\cdot}9 \times 4 \times d}{\pi d^2 \mu} = \frac{360 \times 7 \times 48}{22 \times 5 \times 2{\cdot}42} = 456.$$

The flow will therefore be streamline, and provided wc/kl is greater than 10, expression (58) will be applicable if the effect of the viscosity gradient in the boundary layer is neglected.

Hence, $Hd/k\theta = 1{\cdot}75(wc/kl)^{\frac{1}{3}}$, where $\theta = (60+30)/2 = 45$ F.°

Heat to be abstracted from the oil $= wc(140-110) = 30wc$ B.Th.U./hr.

So the heat H to be abstracted per ft.² of pipe surface $= \dfrac{30wc}{\pi dl}$.

Hence

$$Hd/k\theta = \frac{30wcd}{\pi dl \times k\theta} = \frac{30}{\pi \times 45} \times \frac{wc}{kl} = 1{\cdot}75(wc/kl)^{\frac{1}{3}}$$

or $(wc/kl)^{\frac{2}{3}} = 8{\cdot}25$ and $\frac{2}{3}\log(wc/kl) = \log 8{\cdot}25 = 0{\cdot}92$, whence $\log(wc/kl) = 1{\cdot}38$ and $wc/kl = 24$.

And

$$l = \frac{90 \times 0{\cdot}5}{24k} = \frac{45}{19{\cdot}2} = 2{\cdot}3 \text{ ft.}$$

FLOW ACROSS A SINGLE CYLINDER

Many measurements have been made of heat transfer by forced convection for flow across isolated cylinders, ranging from fine wires to several inches diameter. In this case the heat transfer

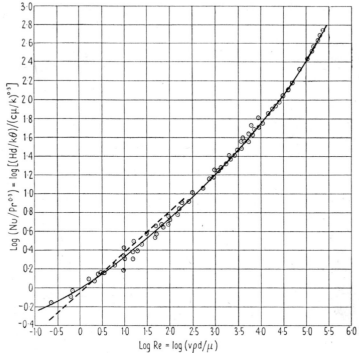

FIG. 37. Main curve for forced convection for a fluid flowing across an isolated cylinder. The full line shows the mean curve through the experimental points ⊙s for gases; the dotted line is the mean curve for liquids.

coefficient varies along the perimeter of the cylinder, being bigger upstream and downstream than at the sides, and the correlations which follow are in terms of the mean heat transfer coefficient for the entire perimeter, which for practical purposes is what is usually required. The experimental range for air covers tempera-ture differences up to 1,000 F.°, velocities up to nearly 100 ft./sec., with Re from about 0·2 to 2×10^5. There are a few results for liquids, mainly from Davis's [10, 11] and Piret's [12] experi-ments with wires, but the range of Re is only from about 0·1 to 2. If, however, $\log(Nu/Pr^{0.3})$ is plotted against $\log Re$, as in Fig. 37, the results for liquids, so far as they extend, are not far from those for gases. In calculating Nu, Pr, and Re, the physical constants are taken at the mean film temperature, i.e. one half the sum of the mean fluid temperature and the mean pipe surface temperature. It will be seen that the slope of the curve gradually increases as Re increases. Hilpert [13], who carried out a systematic series of experiments for cylinders of different diameters in air, found that his results could be expressed as

$$Nu = C(Re)^m. \qquad (62)$$

The values of C and m for different ranges of Re are given in Table VI.

TABLE VI. *Values of Constants for Use in Expression* (62)

Re	C	m
1–4	0·891	0·330
4–40	0·821	0·385
40–4,000	0·615	0·466
4,000–40,000	0·174	0·618
40,000–400,000	0·024	0·805

Hilpert's results agree very closely with the mean curve for gases in Fig. 37; but since between $Re = 1,000$ and $100,000$ this curve is expressed almost within the limits of experimental error by

$$Nu = 0·26Re^{0·6}Pr^{0·3}, \qquad (63)$$

or, for gases, by $\qquad Nu = 0·24Re^{0·6}, \qquad (64)$

it is simpler to use this overall equation. For values of Re outside the range to which (64) is applicable, Hilpert's equations may be used. Coefficients of heat transfer calculated from (64) are given in Fig. 38 for mass velocities up to 30,000 lb./ft.² hr. In calculating these k and μ have been taken at a 'film' temperature, i.e. a mean temperature of cylinder and air, of 250° F. The factors by which they should be multiplied to correct them to film temperatures from 0° F. to 3,000° F. are shown in the subsidiary curve. It will be noticed that, as for flow through pipes, the heat transfer coefficient for any given mass flow and cylinder diameter increases with increase of temperature.

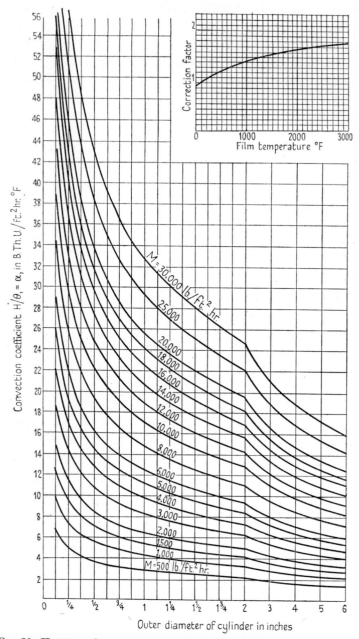

FIG. 38. Heat transfer coefficients for air flowing at different mass velocities across an isolated cylinder (mean film temperature 250° F.).

Effect of inclination of cylinder to fluid stream. There is evidence that for an air stream striking a cylinder at an angle of 45° the heat transfer is about three-quarters, and for flow parallel to the axis about one-half, that for flow at right angles to the axis.

Flow across Banks or Nests of Pipes

For flow across banks of pipes, whether these are 'staggered' or arranged 'in line', the experimental data agree well with the expression:

$$Nu = 0.33\,C_H\,Re^{0.6}\,Pr^{0.3}, \tag{65}$$

which, for air or diatomic gases, for which $Pr = 0.74$, reduces to

$$Nu = 0.30\,C_H\,Re^{0.6}. \tag{66}$$

The above expressions hold only for banks more than five or six rows in depth, i.e. banks containing more than five or six layers of pipes in the direction of flow, as they would in most commercial plant. This is because the heat transfer coefficient in the first few rows of a bank of pipes, for which the final flow pattern has not yet developed, is usually somewhat less than that for subsequent rows.

The physical constants, k and μ, are, as for flow across a single pipe, to be evaluated at the mean film temperature, i.e. half the sum of the mean fluid temperature and the mean wall temperature, and the characteristic linear dimension is the pipe diameter. Since the cross-section of a bank of pipes is not uniform, neither is the velocity of the gases flowing through it; and the linear velocity, $v_{\max}$, or mass velocity, $M_{\max}$, used in calculating Re in (65) or (66), is to be based on the minimum flow area, i.e. on the area at the narrowest restriction. For in-line arrangements this is between adjacent pipes of any row, so that if X is the centre-to-centre distance between the rows of pipes in the direction of flow, and Y is the centre-to-centre distance between the pipes of any row at right angles to the direction of flow, $v_{\max}$ or $M_{\max}$ is $Y/(Y-d)$ times the oncoming, or free flow, velocity, v or M. For staggered arrangements the minimum free-flow area may be either between adjacent pipes of any row, when the velocity to be taken is, as above, $Yv/(Y-d)$, or, if X/Y is so small that

$\sqrt{(4X^2+Y^2)} < (Y+d)$, between diagonally opposed pipes, when

the velocity to be taken is $\dfrac{Y}{\sqrt{(4X^2+Y^2)}-2d}v$.

The curves of Fig. 38 can be used to find the heat transfer coefficients for pipe banks. All that is necessary is to multiply them by $\dfrac{0\cdot30C_H}{0\cdot24} = 1\cdot25C_H$, of course using $M_{\max}$ in place of M.

Values of C_H for the different arrangements shown in Figs.

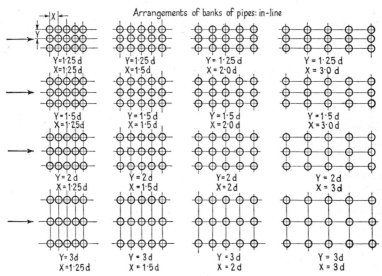

Arrangements of banks of pipes: in-line

Y=1·25d
X=1·25d

Y=1·25d
X=1·5d

Y=1·25d
X=2·0d

Y=1·25d
X=3·0d

Y=1·5d
X=1·25d

Y=1·5d
X=1·5d

Y=1·5d
X=2·0d

Y=1·5d
X=3·0d

Y=2d
X=1·25d

Y=2d
X=1·5d

Y=2d
X=2d

Y=2d
X=3d

Y=3d
X=1·25d

Y=3d
X=1·5d

Y=3d
X=2d

Y=3d
X=3d

FIG. 39. Diagram of in-line pipe bank arrangement.

39 (in-line) and 40 (staggered), based on the work of Huge [14], Pierson [15], Grimison [16], Kuznetzoff and Lokshin [17], are given in Tables VII and VIII. It will be seen that for the in-line arrangements C_H does not differ much from unity except when Re is small, and when also the distance Y between the pipes in any one row is more than $1\cdot5d$, and the distance X between the rows is less than $2d$. In the extreme case, when $Re = 2,000$, $Y = 3d$, and $X = 1\cdot5d$ or less, C_H may fall as low as $0\cdot66$. For the staggered arrangements, C_H, although again as a rule not far from unity, tends, in contradistinction to the in-line arrangements, to be above unity for low values of Re and close spacing,

rising to 1·26 in the most extreme case. Thus, for practical work, C_H, especially in preliminary calculations, can often be assumed equal to 1.

Comparison with flow across a single cylinder. It is interesting to compare the heat transfer, for the ranges in which C_H can be taken as nearly unity, with that for flow across a single

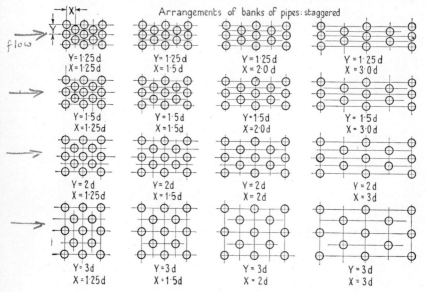

Fig. 40. Diagram of staggered pipe bank arrangement.

cylinder, for the same oncoming velocity. Thus, for $Y = 1·25d$, and $X = 1·25d$ to $3d$, the coefficient of heat transfer is, for a given oncoming velocity, about $3\frac{1}{4}$ times that for a single cylinder. For $Y = 1·5d$, and $X = 1·25d$ to $3d$, it is about $2\frac{1}{2}$ times. For $Y = 2d$, and $X = 2d$ to $3d$, or, at high Re, $1·25d$ to $3d$, it is about 1·9 times; and for $Y = 3d$, and similar ranges of X, about 1·6 times.

Pressure drop across banks of pipes. The pressure drop, Δp, indicating the fan power required to move the fluid across a bank of pipes, is often an important practical consideration. It can be expressed by

$$\Delta p = C_f n \rho v_{\max}^2 \times 10^{-3} \text{ in. of water} \qquad (67)$$

or

$$\Delta p = 5 \cdot 2 C_f \, n \rho v_{\mathrm{max}}^2 \times 10^{-3} \text{ lb. per ft.}^2 \text{ cross-section of bank,} \quad (68)$$

where C_f is a friction factor depending upon the pipe arrangement, n the number of rows of pipes in the bank, and v is the velocity in ft./sec. through the minimum flow area. Values of C_f based on Grimison's [16] correlations of Huge's [14] and Pierson's [15] work, covering a range of Re from 2,000 to 40,000, are given in Tables VII and VIII. These values, which are thought to be the most accurate available, agree fairly well over the greater part of the range with those of other investigators.

Effect of pipe spacing upon heat transfer and pressure drop. It will be seen from Tables VII and VIII that with both in-line and staggered arrangements, for any given value of Y (distance between the tubes at right angles to the direction of flow), the ratio of the heat transfer factor, C_H, to the friction factor, C_f, in general decreases as X is increased. This is particularly noticeable for in-line arrangements, the rate of decrease becoming more rapid as Y increases. For staggered arrangements the decrease is appreciable for small values of Y, but as Y increases it becomes less marked, and for $Y = 3d$ there is a slight increase.

Since both heat transfer and pressure drop are directly proportional to the number of rows it is generally economical both in space and pressure drop to pack the rows of tubes as closely as practicable.

The effect of altering the distance, Y, between the tubes at right angles to the direction of flow, is less simple to explain. To begin with, the velocity upon which (66) is based, for any given oncoming velocity varies with Y.

Thus for either in-line or staggered arrangements, provided the narrowest restriction is between adjacent pipes of any row, the appropriate velocity or mass velocity for

$$Y = 1 \cdot 25d; \ 1 \cdot 5d; \ 2d; \ 3d$$

is respectively 5; 3; 2; 1·5 times the oncoming velocity or mass velocity. Hence the pressure drop, which is proportional to v^2,

TABLE VII

Heat Transfer Factor C_H and Friction Factor C_f for Flow over Pipe Banks. In-line Arrangements

Re	X = 1.25d			X = 1.5d			X = 2.0d			X = 3.0d		
	C_H	C_f	C_H/C_f	C_H	C_f	C_H/C_f	C_H	C_f	C_H/C_f	C_H	C_f	C_H/C_f
							Y = 1.25d					
2,000	1·06	1·68	0·63	1·06	1·74	0·61	1·07	2·04	0·52	1·00	2·28	0·44
8,000	1·04	1·68	0·62	1·05	1·74	0·60	1·03	2·04	0·50	0·98	2·28	0·43
20,000	1·00	1·44	0·69	1·00	1·56	0·64	1·00	1·74	0·57	0·95	2·04	0·47
40,000	1·00	1·20	0·83	1·00	1·32	0·76	0·96	1·56	0·62	0·93	1·80	0·52
							Y = 1.5d					
2,000	0·95	0·79	1·20	0·95	0·97	0·98	1·03	1·20	0·86	1·03	1·56	0·66
8,000	0·96	0·83	1·16	0·96	0·96	1·00	1·01	1·20	0·84	1·01	1·56	0·65
20,000	0·96	0·84	1·14	0·96	0·96	1·00	1·00	1·13	0·89	0·98	1·46	0·67
40,000	0·96	0·74	1·30	0·96	0·85	1·13	0·98	1·02	0·96	0·95	1·27	0·75
							Y = 2.0d					
2,000	0·73	0·29	2·51	0·73	0·44	1·66	0·98	0·66	1·49	1·08	1·02	1·06
8,000	0·83	0·35	2·37	0·83	0·48	1·73	1·00	0·67	1·49	1·02	1·02	1·00
20,000	0·90	0·38	2·37	0·90	0·49	1·84	1·00	0·66	1·52	1·00	0·88	1·14
40,000	0·96	0·41	2·34	0·96	0·48	2·00	1·01	0·62	1·63	0·97	0·77	1·26
							Y = 3.0d					
2,000	0·66	0·12	5·50	0·66	0·22	3·00	0·95	0·40	2·38	1·00	0·62	1·61
8,000	0·81	0·20	4·05	0·81	0·28	2·89	1·00	0·43	2·32	1·00	0·60	1·67
20,000	0·91	0·22	4·14	0·91	0·30	3·03	1·02	0·42	2·43	1·00	0·55	1·82
40,000	1·00	0·25	4·00	1·00	0·30	3·33	1·04	0·38	2·74	0·98	0·46	2·13

Table VIII

Heat Transfer Factor C_H and Friction Factor C_f for Flow over Pipe Banks. Staggered Arrangements

Re	X = 1·25d			X = 1·5d			X = 2·0d			X = 3·0d		
	C_H	C_f	C_H/C_f	C_H	C_f	C_H/C_f	C_H	C_f	C_H/C_f	C_H	C_f	C_H/C_f
Y = 1·25d												
2,000	1·21	2·52	0·48	1·16	2·58	0·45	1·06	2·58	0·41	0·96	2·64	0·36
8,000	1·11	1·98	0·56	1·10	2·10	0·52	1·02	2·16	0·47	0·95	2·28	0·42
20,000	1·06	1·56	0·68	1·05	1·74	0·60	1·00	1·92	0·52	0·93	2·16	0·43
40,000	1·03	1·26	0·82	1·02	1·50	0·68	0·98	1·68	0·58	0·91	1·98	0·46
Y = 1·5d												
2,000	1·17	1·80	0·65	1·15	1·80	0·64	1·08	1·80	0·60	1·02	1·92	0·53
8,000	1·10	1·44	0·76	1·06	1·50	0·70	1·00	1·56	0·64	0·96	1·56	0·62
20,000	1·04	1·10	0·95	1·02	1·16	0·88	0·98	1·32	0·74	0·94	1·44	0·65
40,000	0·99	0·88	1·13	0·98	0·96	1·02	0·94	1·08	0·87	0·91	1·20	0·76
Y = 2·0d												
2,000	1·22	1·56	0·78	1·18	1·50	0·79	1·12	1·44	0·78	1·08	1·32	0·82
8,000	1·12	1·19	0·94	1·10	1·16	0·95	1·04	1·14	0·91	1·01	1·13	0·89
20,000	1·09	0·96	1·14	1·07	0·96	1·11	1·01	0·96	1·05	0·97	0·96	1·01
40,000	1·04	0·77	1·35	1·01	0·79	1·28	0·97	0·82	1·18	0·93	0·84	1·11
Y = 3·0d												
2,000	1·26	1·50	0·84	1·26	1·38	0·91	1·18	1·13	1·05	1·13	1·02	1·11
8,000	1·16	1·08	1·07	1·16	1·04	1·11	1·11	0·96	1·16	1·06	0·90	1·18
20,000	1·14	0·86	1·33	1·13	0·84	1·35	1·10	0·78	1·41	1·02	0·74	1·38
40,000	1·10	0·70	1·57	1·09	0·68	1·60	1·05	0·65	1·62	1·00	0·60	1·67

or M^2, will for given oncoming velocity be in the ratio of

$$C_f : C_f \times \left(\frac{3}{5}\right)^2 : C_f \times \left(\frac{2}{5}\right)^2 : C_f \times \left(\frac{1 \cdot 5}{5}\right)^2,$$

the appropriate values for C_f being taken from the tables.

Heat transfer: in-line arrangements. Banks of pipes are so commonly used in heat exchangers that average ratios of heat transfer and pressure drop, and of heat transfer to pressure drop, are worked out below for the experimental ranges of pipe arrangement and Re, i.e. the various combinations of X and $Y = 1 \cdot 25d$, $1 \cdot 5d$, $2d$, and $3d$ for Re 2,000 to 40,000.

The heat transfer per unit area of cross-section for in-line arrangements is, for given diameter, proportional to $C_H \times M^{0 \cdot 6}$ or, assuming ρ not to vary, to $C_H v_{\max}^{0 \cdot 6}$, and to the surface area of the pipes in any row.

For $Y = 1 \cdot 25d$, $1 \cdot 5d$, $2d$, $3d$, $v_{\max}^{0 \cdot 6}$ is, for given oncoming velocity, in the ratio of

$$2 \cdot 63 : 1 \cdot 93 : 1 \cdot 52 : 1 \cdot 28$$

or $1 : 0 \cdot 73 : 0 \cdot 58 : 0 \cdot 49$

The surface area per row is in the ratio of

$$4/5 : 2/3 : 1/2 : 1/3$$

or $1 : 0 \cdot 83 : 0 \cdot 625 : 0 \cdot 42.$

Mean values of C_H for Re 2,000 to 40,000 are from Table VII, for the different values of Y, seen to be:

for $X = 1 \cdot 25d$ $1 \cdot 03,\ 0 \cdot 96,\ 0 \cdot 86,\ 0 \cdot 85$

or $1 : 0 \cdot 93 : 0 \cdot 84 : 0 \cdot 83$

for $X = 1 \cdot 5d$ $1 \cdot 03,\ 0 \cdot 96,\ 0 \cdot 86,\ 0 \cdot 85$

or $1 : 0 \cdot 93 : 0 \cdot 84 : 0 \cdot 83$

for $X = 2d$ $1 \cdot 02,\ 1 \cdot 01,\ 1 \cdot 00,\ 1 \cdot 00$

or $1 : 0 \cdot 99 : 0 \cdot 98 : 0 \cdot 98$

for $X = 3d$ $0 \cdot 97,\ 0 \cdot 99,\ 1 \cdot 02,\ 1 \cdot 00$

or $1 : 1 \cdot 02 : 1 \cdot 05 : 1 \cdot 03.$

These ratios do not vary much, although they show slight increase with increasing X. Averaging them gives:

$$1:0.97:0.93:0.92.$$

Multiplying by the $v_{max}^{0.6}$ ratios and the area ratios leads finally to heat transfer per unit area of cross-section for the same oncoming velocity for

$$Y = 1.25d, \ 1.5d, \ 2d, \ 3d$$

in the ratio of $\qquad 1:0.59:0.34:0.19.$ (69)

Pressure drop: in-line arrangements. With $X = 1.25d$, for the different values of Y, the pressure drop for the in-line arrangements is in the ratio:

for $Re = 2000 \quad 1.68:0.79\times\left(\dfrac{3}{5}\right)^2:0.29\times\left(\dfrac{2}{5}\right)^2:0.12\times\left(\dfrac{1.5}{5}\right)^2$

or $\qquad\qquad\qquad 1: \quad 0.170 \quad : \quad 0.028 \quad : \quad 0.006$

for $Re = 8000 \quad 1.68:0.83\times\left(\dfrac{3}{5}\right)^2:0.35\times\left(\dfrac{2}{5}\right)^2:0.20\times\left(\dfrac{1.5}{5}\right)^2$

or $\qquad\qquad\qquad 1: \quad 0.179 \quad : \quad 0.033 \quad : \quad 0.011$

for $Re = 20000 \quad 1.44:0.84\times\left(\dfrac{3}{5}\right)^2:0.38\times\left(\dfrac{2}{5}\right)^2:0.22\times\left(\dfrac{1.5}{5}\right)^2$

or $\qquad\qquad\qquad 1: \quad 0.210 \quad : \quad 0.042 \quad : \quad 0.014$

for $Re = 40000 \quad 1.20:0.74\times\left(\dfrac{3}{5}\right)^2:0.41\times\left(\dfrac{2}{5}\right)^2:0.25\times\left(\dfrac{1.5}{5}\right)^2$

or $\qquad\qquad\qquad 1: \quad 0.222 \quad : \quad 0.055 \quad : \quad 0.019.$

This gives mean ratios for Re 2,000 to 20,000

for $X = 1.25d \qquad 1:0.195:0.040:0.012$
for $X = 1.5d \qquad\ 1:0.213:0.048:0.016$
for $X = 2d \qquad\ \ \ 1:0.223:0.057:0.020$
for $X = 3d \qquad\ \ \ 1:0.251:0.070:0.024.$

It will be noticed that, as for C_H, there is a slight increase in the pressure-drop ratios with increase in the value of X. The average ratios for X 1.25 to $3d$ for

$$Y = 1.25d, \ 1.5d, \ 2d, \ 3d$$

are $\qquad\qquad 1:0.221:0.053:0.018.$ (70)

(Heat transfer)/(pressure drop) is thus in the ratio of (69) to (70), i.e. $\qquad\qquad 1:2.7:6.4:10.6.$ (71)

The heat transfer per unit area of cross-section for a given oncoming velocity, by (69), is about 5 times greater for $Y = 1\cdot25d$ than for $Y = 3d$, but the pressure drop, by (70), is 55 times greater. Thus the conditions for high heat transfer per unit area of cross-section and for low pressure drop are opposed. If considerations of space are the more important, the heat exchanger can be made small, but the pressure drop will be high. If fan power is the more important, the pressure drop can be kept low, but the size of the exchanger will be bigger.†

Heat transfer: staggered arrangements. For the staggered arrangements, if the ratios of heat transfer and pressure drop are worked out in a similar manner for the different values of X, it is found that for a given oncoming velocity the heat transfer per unit area of cross-section for the different values of Y is in the ratio

$$1:0\cdot59:0\cdot34:0\cdot18, \tag{72}$$

almost the same as for the in-line arrangements.

Pressure drop: staggered arrangements. The corresponding pressure drops are in the ratio of

$$1:0\cdot248:0\cdot086:0\cdot042 \tag{73}$$

and (heat transfer)/(pressure drop) in the ratio of (72) to (73), i.e.,

$$1:2\cdot4:4\cdot0:4\cdot3. \tag{74}$$

These increase less rapidly than for in-line arrangements, because, although the heat transfer falls off at the same rate as for the in-line arrangements, the pressure drop falls off less rapidly.

Comparison of in-line and staggered arrangements. It will be seen from Table IX, which gives the ratios of C_H/C_f (in-line) to C_H/C_f (staggered), that for the whole range of values of X and Y, C_H/C_f (in-line) is bigger than C_H/C_f (staggered), the ratio increasing as Y increases and X decreases. It varies from $3\cdot69$ for $Y = 3d$ and $X = 1\cdot25d$, to approximately $1\cdot10$ for all values of X at $Y = 1\cdot25d$. On the other hand, the actual values of

---

† It is however interesting to note that if, as the tubes are packed closer together, the oncoming velocity is so reduced as to keep the total heat transfer per square foot of cross-section constant, the ratio of heat transfer to friction improves. But in this case only relatively small quantities of fluid can be dealt with unless the cross-sectional area of the exchanger is increased.

TABLE IX. *Ratio of Mean Values of C_H/C_f in-line to C_H/C_f staggered.*

	$X = 1.25d$	$X = 1.5d$	$X = 2.0d$	$X = 3.0d$
$Y = 1.25d$	0·69/0·64 = 1·08	0·65/0·56 = 1·16	0·55/0·50 = 1·10	0·47/0·42 = 1·12
$Y = 1.5d$	1·20/0·87 = 1·38	1·04/0·81 = 1·28	0·89/0·71 = 1·25	0·68/0·64 = 1·06
$Y = 2.0d$	2·40/1·05 = 2·29	1·81/1·03 = 1·76	1·53/1·03 = 1·49	1·12/0·96 = 1·17
$Y = 3.0d$	4·42/1·20 = 3·69	2·99/1·24 = 2·41	2·47/1·31 = 1·89	1·81/1·34 = 1·35

C_H*tend to be somewhat bigger for the staggered arrangement than for the in-line, especially for big values of Y and small values of X. It is once again the conflict between heat transfer and pressure drop for any given cross-section. Other things being the same, staggered arrangements are likely to give slightly greater heat transfer, but usually at a disproportionate increase in pressure drop.

Effect of angle of impact of air upon heat transfer. Lokshin [18], and Ornatski [19], independently, have investigated the heat transfer for banks of pipes in a stream of air striking at angles 15 to 90 degrees to the axes. A range of Re from 5,000 to 40,000 was covered for $X = Y = 2d$.

For banks of more than about 5 rows, with the results expressed as $Nu = \text{constant} \times Re^{0.6}$, the constants for the different angles of impact were:

TABLE X. *Constants, C, in the Equation $Nu = CRe^{0.6}$ for Oblique Flow of Air across Pipe Banks of $X = Y = 2d$.*

	$90°$	$80°$	$70°$	$60°$	$45°$	$30°$	$15°$
In-line	0·29	0·29	0·28	0·27	0·24	0·20	0·12
Staggered	0·32	0·32	0·31	0·30	0·25	0·17	0·13

Since, for both in-line and staggered arrangements with $X = Y = 2d$, C_H over the range in Re 5,000 to 40,000 is nearly 1, it will be seen that the results for 90 degrees agree very closely with (66) in which the constant is $0.30C_H$. Until the angle of impact is below 60 degrees (66) can be used without much error, but at 45 degrees the heat transfer has decreased by roughly 20 per cent., at 30 degrees by 40 per cent., and at 15 degrees by 60 per cent. Both Lokshin and Ornatski found that the heat transfer in the first row of the in-line banks was about 30 per cent.

less than the average for the subsequent rows. This agrees with the previous American work, the difference, however, varying with the spacing. For staggered arrangements Lokshin found the heat transfer in the first row was about 12 per cent. less than in subsequent rows.

General expressions for heat transfer, pressure drop, and their ratio. If Y is written as yd, the effective velocity v_{max}, except in very extreme cases, is $vy/(y-1)$, where v is the oncoming velocity, or the total volume flowing divided by the cross-sectional area of the bank (see p. 132). The area of the pipes per row, per unit area of cross-section, is π/y.

Hence, H_s/θ, the heat transfer coefficient per row, per unit area of bank cross-section, is proportional to

$$C_H\left(\frac{y}{y-1}\right)^{0.6}\times\frac{1}{y}\times(v\rho)^{0.6}\frac{1}{d^{0.4}}. \tag{75}$$

Δp, the pressure drop per row, is proportional to

$$C_f\rho v^2\left(\frac{y}{y-1}\right)^2, \tag{76}$$

as is also the fan power per row.

From these two expressions the variation of H_s/θ and Δp with v, d, and y can be worked out; and, if in $v\rho$ only v varies while ρ remains constant, the ratio of H_s/θ to Δp for different conditions can also be found, being proportional to

$$\frac{C_H}{C_f}\left(\frac{y-1}{y}\right)^{1.4}\times\frac{1}{v^{1.4}}\times\frac{1}{y}\times\frac{1}{d^{0.4}}. \tag{77}$$

For example, suppose that, in a bank of given d, X, and Y, across the pipes of which air is flowing, v is increased to av and it is desired to keep the difference between inlet and outlet air temperatures, Δt, unchanged by altering the number of rows of pipes n.

The heat transfer coefficient per row, per unit area of bank cross-section, H'_s/θ, which is proportional to $C'_H v^{0.6}_{max}$ will become $(C'_H/C_H)\times a^{0.6}\times H_s/\theta$, where C_H and C'_H are the heat transfer factors for Re corresponding to v_{max} and $(av)_{max}$ respectively. If the number of rows of pipes is increased b times, the heat transfer coefficient per unit cross-section for the whole bank will be increased $(C'_H/C_H) \times a^{0\cdot6} \times b$ times. But since the mass velocity has increased a times, to keep Δt unchanged

$$(C'_H/C_H) \times a^{0\cdot6} \times b = a \quad \text{or} \quad b = (C_H/C'_H) \times a^{0\cdot4}.$$

The ratio of heat transfer to pressure drop $(H'_s/\theta)/\Delta p'$ for velocity av will, from (77), become

$$\left(\frac{C'_H}{C_H} \times \frac{C_f}{C'_f} \times \frac{1}{a^{1\cdot4}}\right) \times (H_s/\theta)/\Delta p.$$

Since fan power is proportional to $\Delta p \times v$, the ratio of heat transfer to fan power will become $\dfrac{C'_H}{C_H} \times \dfrac{C_f}{C'_f} \times \dfrac{1}{a^{2\cdot4}}$ times its original value.

Again, suppose that in two banks consisting of pipes of the same diameter, but differently arranged (1) $Y = yd$, $X = xd$ and (2) $Y' = y'd$, $X' = x'd$, it is desired to keep Δt the same for given oncoming velocity, i.e. for given mass flow per unit area of bank cross-section, by changing the number of rows from n to an.

$$nC_H\left(\frac{y}{y-1}\right)^{0\cdot6} \times \frac{1}{y} = anC'_H\left(\frac{y'}{y'-1}\right)^{0\cdot6} \times \frac{1}{y'}$$

or
$$a = \frac{C_H(y'-1)^{0\cdot6}}{C'_H(y-1)^{0\cdot6}} \times \left(\frac{y'}{y}\right)^{0\cdot4},$$

where C_H and C'_H are the heat transfer factors corresponding to the two arrangements and the given mass velocity.

The ratios of heat transfer to pressure drop $(H'_s/\theta)/\Delta p'$: $(H_s/\theta)/\Delta p$, or, since the volume flow per unit area of bank cross-section does not change, of heat transfer to fan power, will be in the ratio of

$$\frac{C_f}{aC'_f}\left[\frac{y(y'-1)}{y'(y-1)}\right]^2 = \frac{C'_H}{C_H}\frac{C_f}{C'_f}\left(\frac{y'-1}{y-1}\right)^{1\cdot4}\left(\frac{y}{y'}\right)^{2\cdot4}.$$

The effects of other variations can be worked out in a similar way.

HEAT TRANSFER FOR FLOW OVER PLANE SURFACES

For a plane surface the characteristic dimension upon which forced convection depends is the length of the plate in the direction of flow. Most of the measurements have been made with a plate in alinement with one of the walls of a duct, or, if the plate has been freely exposed, it has often had an unheated leading-in piece. In the latter case, some workers have correlated their results with the total length of plate and leading-in piece as the characteristic linear dimension in Nu and Re, introducing also a factor depending upon the ratio of plate length to leading-in piece length.

Experiments on air [20, 21] and water [22] agree well in the turbulent region, which in this case corresponds to Re above about 2×10^4, with the expression

$$Nu = 0 \cdot 036 Re^{0 \cdot 8} Pr^{0 \cdot 33}. \tag{78}$$

For air, and other gases with similar Prandtl number, this becomes

$$Nu = 0 \cdot 032 Re^{0 \cdot 8}. \tag{79}$$

In the above equations, it is the length of the plate which is taken in calculating Nu and Re, with k and μ taken at the mean film temperature.

For streamline flow [21, 23] the corresponding expressions are

$$Nu = 0 \cdot 66 Re^{0 \cdot 5} Pr^{0 \cdot 33}, \tag{80}$$

or for gases,

$$Nu = 0 \cdot 60 Re^{0 \cdot 5}. \tag{81}$$

HEAT TRANSFER FOR FLOW OVER SPHERE

For a sphere in a current of air [24], for Re between 50 and 150,000,

$$Nu = 0 \cdot 34 Re^{0 \cdot 6} \tag{82}$$

with the diameter of the sphere as the characteristic linear dimension, and with k and μ taken at the mean film temperature.

It is interesting to note that in this case it can be shown theoretically that as v tends to zero Nu tends to a value of 2, or H/θ to $2k/d$. This, for a sphere in air, and a mean temperature of, say, $200°$ F., is equal to $0 \cdot 035/d$, which works out at $4 \cdot 2$, $0 \cdot 42$, and $0 \cdot 042$ B.Th.U./ft.^{2} hr. $°$F. for spheres of diameter $0 \cdot 1$ in., 1 in., and 10 in. respectively.

DETERMINATION OF MEAN TEMPERATURE DIFFERENCE IN HEAT EXCHANGERS

In a heat exchanger the temperature difference between the two fluids flowing on opposite sides of the boundary wall usually varies with position; hence, to calculate the heat transfer, some mean value must be decided upon, which in general depends upon the form of the heat exchanger.

In parallel flow heat exchangers, one fluid flows through a series of pipes, usually parallel, and another fluid flows in the same direction over the outside of the pipes; in contra-flow exchangers the fluids inside and outside the pipes flow in opposite directions. For both these arrangements the temperature conditions are the same for all the pipes, and, if the overall heat transfer coefficient is assumed to be constant along the length of any one pipe, the logarithmic mean overall temperature difference $\theta_m = (\theta_1 - \theta_2)/\log_e(\theta_1/\theta_2)$ is to be taken, where θ_1 is the temperature difference between the two fluids at one end, θ_2 at the other.

Provided the spacing is not very wide, the heat transfer coefficient on the outside of the pipes can be estimated from the usual formula for flow through a pipe, using the mean hydraulic diameter in calculating Nu and Re, but, of course, calculating the heat transfer on the actual pipe surface. If the pipes are very far apart the heat transfer would probably be obtained more closely by taking the value of the coefficient as one-half that for flow at the same velocity across a single isolated pipe of the same diameter (see p. 132).

In cross-flow heat exchangers the two fluids flow in perpendicular directions, usually one through and one across a nest of pipes. If it is assumed that the fluid on the outside of the pipes becomes so well mixed that its temperature over any given cross-section of the exchanger is uniform, the temperature conditions will be the same for all the pipes in any one row, but will vary from row to row. For the fluid flowing through the pipes the temperature will also vary with length along the pipe. The computation of the mean temperature difference is thus in this case somewhat complicated, but it has been given by Smith [25], for a range of temperature difference ratios P, Q, and R, defined as $P = (t_1 - t_2)/(t_1 - t_1')$, $Q = (t_2' - t_1')/(t_1 - t_1')$ and $R = \theta_m/(t_1 - t_1')$, where t_1 and t_2 are the inlet and outlet temperatures of the fluid flowing across the pipes and t_1' is the inlet temperature and t_2' the mean outlet temperature of the fluid flowing through the pipes.

Smith's curves of constant values of P in coordinates of Q and R, and of constant values of R in coordinates of P and Q, are plotted in Fig. 41.

In problems where $(P+Q)$ is small, the arithmetic mean temperature difference, $[(t_1-t_1')+(t_2-t_2')]/2$, may be used. When $(P+Q)$ is less than $0\cdot6$ the error thus involved is less than 5

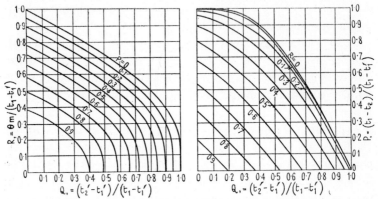

FIG. 41. Mean temperature differences for cross flow.

per cent.; when $(P+Q)$ is less than $0\cdot7$ the error is less than 10 per cent.

USE OF FINS OR RIBS

The rate of heat transfer from a surface can be made greater by finning or ribbing it and so increasing the effective surface area. Ideally the fins should be at the same temperature as the original surface, so that, assuming the heat transfer coefficient not to alter, the heat transfer would be increased in the ratio of S'/S, where S' is the total area of the finned, S that of the unfinned, surface. Actually there is always a temperature gradient from base to tip of the fins, so that, although the heat transfer coefficient may actually be bigger for the fins than for the original surface, the heat transfer is usually increased by less than S'/S times. Owing to the large increase in the surface area possible, however, substantial advantages can be gained. For instance, the surface area per foot length of a 1-in. pipe is $\pi/12$ ft.[2] If fins projecting $\frac{1}{2}$ in. from the pipe are fixed along it at intervals of $\frac{1}{4}$ in. their area per foot length would be $6\pi/12$ ft.[2], i.e. six times the original area. Fins can be used with special advantage when the heat transfer coefficient is much smaller on one side of a partition than on the other, or where the maximum possible rate of heat transfer is desired from a limited base area.

Unfortunately, formulae for heat transfer and fin efficiency cannot be reduced to simple forms, and their detailed consideration is beyond the scope of such a book as this. The interested reader is referred to a Symposium on Finned Surfaces held by the American Society of Mechanical Engineers [26].

Convection at Very High Gas Velocities

In all the cases of forced convection so far considered, gases have been supposed to behave as incompressible. At very high flow rates this, as explained on p. 66, may no longer be justifiable [27]. The study of forced convection with substantial changes of density during flow has as yet received little experimental study, although it frequently occurs in practice, as in expansion nozzles and high-speed flow generally. For speeds given by Mach numbers between 0·2 and 1·0, i.e. for velocities 0·2 to 1·0 times the velocity in the gas of sound waves of small amplitude, forced convection in a pipe follows the law

$$Nu = 0{\cdot}025 Re^{0{\cdot}77}, \tag{83}$$

where the temperature difference in Nu is the difference between the tube-wall temperature and the so-called adiabatic wall temperature, which is the temperature the wall would attain if there were no heat transfer, given in absolute degrees by

$$\{T + (rv^2/2cgJ)\},$$

where T is the absolute gas temperature, J the mechanical equivalent of heat, and r a so-called 'recovery factor' $= 0{\cdot}8{-}1{\cdot}0$.

Example 1

Air at 60° F. flows at 20 ft./sec. across the outside of a pipe. Air is also flowing through the pipe. If the temperature and velocity of the air inside the pipe are respectively 200° F. and 40 ft./sec. at a given cross-section, what will the temperature be at a cross-section 2 ft. farther along the pipe? For simplicity take either outer or inner pipe diameter as 1 in.

Solution. Calculation of outside coefficient of heat transfer, α_0.
Since the temperature of the pipe along the section under consideration is not known, neither is the mean film temperature
at which to take μ and k in calculating α_0. Since, however, the
variation of α_0 with variation in the absolute temperature is
not rapid, little error will be caused by assuming the mean film
temperature on the outside of the pipe to be $[60+(60+200)/2]/2$
$= 95°$ F., say $100°$ F., i.e. by assuming the coefficients of heat
transfer α_0 and α_i on the outside and inside of the pipe to be
approximately equal.

Then from Table XVIII, $\mu = 0.046$ lb./ft. hr., $k = 0.0154$
B.Th.U./ft. hr. °F., and ρ at $60°$ F. $= 0.077$ lb./ft.^{3}

Hence

$$Re = v\rho d/\mu = (20\times 60\times 60\times 0.077)/(12\times 0.046) = 10^4,$$

and, from (64),

$$\alpha_0 = H/\theta = 0.24\times (k/d)\times Re^{0.6} = 11.1 \text{ B.Th.U./ft.}^2 \text{ hr. °F.}$$

Alternatively α_0 could have been read directly from Fig. 38
for a mass velocity of $20\times 60\times 60\times 0.077 = 5,540$ lb./ft.^{2} hr.,
giving a value of 11.9 B.Th.U./ft.^{2} hr. °F. for μ and k taken at
$250°$ F., or a corrected value of $0.91\times 11.9 = 10.9$ B.Th.U./ft.^{2}
hr. °F. for μ and k taken at $100°$ F., which does not differ appreciably from the previous value.

Calculation of inside coefficient of heat transfer, α_i. Since the
temperature drop along a 2-ft. length of pipe is not likely to be
great, μ and k for calculating α_i may be taken at $200°$ F., i.e.
$\mu = 0.052$ lb./ft. hr., $k = 0.0174$ B.Th.U./ft. hr. °F.,

$$\rho \text{ at } 200° \text{ F.} = 0.060 \text{ lb./ft.}^3$$

Hence

$$Re = (40\times 60\times 60\times 0.06)/(12\times 0.052) = 1.38\times 10^4.$$

From (54)

$$\alpha_i = H/\theta = 0.020\times (k/d)\times Re^{0.8} = 8.6 \text{ B.Th.U./ft.}^2 \text{ hr. °F.}$$

Alternatively α_i could have been read directly from Fig. 33
for a mass velocity of $40\times 60\times 60\times 0.06 = 8,640$ lb./ft.^{2} hr.
giving 8.3 B.Th.U./ft.^{2} hr. for μ and k taken at $60°$ F. or

$$1.03\times 8.3 = 8.55 \text{ B.Th.U./ft.}^2 \text{ hr. °F.}$$

for μ and k taken at 200° F., which agrees with the calculated value.

Actually these coefficients would indicate a tube temperature t given by $11 \cdot 1(t-60) = 8 \cdot 6(200-t)$, where $t = 120°$ F., so that the temperature at which μ and k should have been taken in calculating $\alpha_0 = (60+120)/2 = 90°$ F., instead of the 100° F. taken, but this would make no appreciable difference in α_0.

Hence the overall coefficient of heat transfer from inside air to outside air $= 1/[(1/\alpha_0)+(1/\alpha_i)] = 4 \cdot 85$ B.Th.U./ft.^{2} hr. °F., and the required drop, Δt, in the temperature of the inside air will be given by

$$vp \times \pi r^2 \times 0 \cdot 24 \times \Delta t = 4 \cdot 85 \times [(200 - \Delta t/2) - 60] \times 2\pi r \times 2,$$

where $0 \cdot 24$ is the specific heat of air,

i.e. $40 \times 60 \times 60 \times 0 \cdot 06 \times 0 \cdot 24\Delta t = 48 \times 4 \cdot 85 \times (280 - \Delta t)$,

whence $\Delta t = 28$ F.°

Thus the mean temperature at which μ and k should have been taken in calculating $\alpha_i = (200 - 28/2) = 186°$ F., instead of the 200° F. actually taken, but this would make no appreciable difference to α_i.

Example 2

An oil cooler consists of a bank of 200 pipes of $\frac{1}{2}$ in. outside diameter, 20 S.W.G. (0·036 in.) wall thickness, and 4 ft. length, surrounded by a shell of 10 in. inside diameter. Water flows through the pipes at the rate of 10,000 gal. per hour, while 1,500 gal. of oil per hour flows along the outside of the pipes. The inlet water temperature is 64° F., the inlet oil temperature 190° F. Find the outlet oil temperature.

Take the thermal conductivity, k, of the oil as 0·10 B.Th.U./ ft. hr. °F., its specific heat, c, as 0·50 B.Th.U./lb. °F., its specific gravity as 0·93, and its viscosity, μ, in lb./ft. hr. as below:

	65° F.	90° F.	110° F.	130° F.	150° F.	170° F.	190° F.
μ	1,980	660	340	190	120	80	55

Solution. Calculation of heat transfer coefficient, α_w, *on water side.*
Inside pipe diameter $= 0 \cdot 50 - 0 \cdot 072 = 0 \cdot 428$ in.

Cross-sectional area $= \dfrac{200}{144} \times \dfrac{\pi}{4} \times 0 \cdot 428^2 = 0 \cdot 200$ ft.^{2}

For flow through a pipe, the physical properties of the fluid are taken at the mean bulk temperature, which is not known. As an approximation, taking k and μ for water at 65° F. (see Table XVIII), but remembering that a slight adjustment may be required later if the water temperature is found to increase much, $Re = \dfrac{10000 \times 10 \times 0 \cdot 428}{0 \cdot 20 \times 12 \times 2 \cdot 56} = 6950$, since 1 gallon of water weighs 10 lb.

Hence the flow of the water is turbulent, and (53) is applicable, i.e.
$$Hd/k\theta = 0 \cdot 023 Re^{0 \cdot 8} Pr^{0 \cdot 4},$$

$$\frac{H}{\theta} \frac{0 \cdot 428}{12 \times 0 \cdot 346} = 0 \cdot 023 (6950)^{0 \cdot 8} (7 \cdot 41)^{0 \cdot 4},$$

whence $\qquad H/\theta = 592$ B.Th.U./ft.^{2} hr. °F.,[†]

or, expressed per ft.^{2} of the outer surface of the pipe
$$\alpha_w = 592 \times (0 \cdot 428/0 \cdot 50) = 507 \text{ B.Th.U./ft.}^2 \text{ hr. °F.}$$

Calculation of heat transfer coefficient, α_0, *on oil side.* Here the mean hydraulic diameter is to be taken in calculating Nu and Re. This $= 4 \times$ cross-sectional area/wetted perimeter
$$= 4 \left(\frac{\pi}{4} \frac{10^2}{144} - \frac{\pi}{4} \frac{200}{4} \left(\frac{1}{12} \right)^2 \right) \Big/ \left(\frac{\pi \times 10}{12} + \frac{200\pi}{12 \times 2} \right) = 0 \cdot 0378 \text{ ft.}$$

Again, the mean bulk temperature at which k and μ should be taken is not known, but assuming an outlet oil temperature of 170° F., and hence a mean bulk temperature of 180° F.
$$Re = \frac{1500 \times 10 \times 0 \cdot 93 \times 0 \cdot 0378}{0 \cdot 272 \times 65} = 29 \cdot 8.$$

The flow is therefore laminar and α_0 will be given by (60), i.e.
$$Hd/k\theta = 1 \cdot 86 (\mu/\mu_s)^{0 \cdot 14} (Re \, Pr \, d/l)^{\frac{1}{3}}.$$

The value of μ_s depends on the unknown pipe wall temperature t_s. Since most of the thermal resistance is on the oil side, the

---

† Alternatively the curves in Fig. 35 may be used to find H/θ. For $d = 0 \cdot 428$ in., $M = 10000 \times 10/0 \cdot 2 = 500000$ lb./ft.^{2} hr., and bulk temperature 60° F., $H/\theta = 580$ B.Th.U./ft.^{2} hr. °F. For bulk temperature 65° F., H/θ must be multiplied by a correction factor of $1 \cdot 03$, found from the auxiliary curve, giving a corrected value of 597 B.Th.U./ft.^{2} hr. °F. compared with the calculated value of 592.

temperature difference between the oil and the surface will be much greater than that between the water and the surface. The assumed mean temperature of the water was 65° F., and a mean value of 67° F. will be assumed for t_s, making $\mu_s = 1,800$ lb./ft. hr.

$$\frac{H}{\theta}\frac{0\cdot0378}{0\cdot10} = 1\cdot86\left(\frac{65}{1800}\right)^{0\cdot14}\left(29\cdot8\times\frac{0\cdot5\times65}{0\cdot1}\times\frac{0\cdot0378}{4}\right)^{\frac{1}{3}},$$

whence $\qquad H/\theta = \alpha_0 = 13\cdot9$ B.Th.U./ft.^{2} hr. °F.

The overall heat transfer coefficient

$$U = \frac{1}{1/\alpha_w + 1/\alpha_0}$$

$$= 13\cdot5 \text{ B.Th.U./ft.}^2 \text{ hr. °F.}$$

Mean temperature difference, oil to water

$$= (180-65) = 115° \text{ F.}$$

Total surface area $= 200 \times \pi dl = \dfrac{200\times\pi\times4}{2\times12} = 105 \text{ ft.}^2$

∴ Total heat transfer

$$= 13\cdot5\times115\times105 = 164{,}000 \text{ B.Th.U./hr.}$$

Heat capacity of oil

$$= 1500\times10\times0\cdot93\times0\cdot5 \text{ B.Th.U./hr. °F.}$$

$$= 6{,}970 \text{ B.Th.U./hr. °F.}$$

∴ Temperature drop $= \dfrac{164000}{6970} = 23\cdot5 \text{ F.}°$ instead of 20° assumed.

Outlet temperature of oil $= 166\cdot5°$ F.

The values assumed for mean water temperature and mean pipe wall temperature can now be checked.

Rise in water temperature $= 164000/10000\times10 = 1\cdot64$ F.°, and mean water temperature $= 64\cdot8°$ F. A value of 65° F. was assumed when calculating α_w, and clearly no adjustment is necessary.

Mean oil temperature $= (190+166\cdot5)/2 = 178°$ F., and pipe-wall temperature t_s is given by

$$\alpha_w(t_s-65) = \alpha_0(178-t_s),$$

whence $t_s = (178 \times 13 \cdot 9 + 507 \times 65)/(13 \cdot 9 + 507) = 68°$ F., instead of $67°$ F. assumed. Again, no adjustment is necessary.

EXAMPLE 3

Air at $60°$ F. is to be heated to $85°$ F. by passing it across the pipes of a staggered nest, inside which steam is condensing at $212°$ F. The pipes have outer diameter, d, $= \frac{1}{2}$ in., centre to centre spacing, X, $= \frac{3}{4}$ in. $= 1 \cdot 5d$, in the direction of flow and Y, $= 1\frac{1}{2}$ in. $= 3d$, in the transverse direction. If the mass velocity of the air is 8000 lb./hr. per ft.² of total cross-section, find the number of rows of pipes required and the pressure drop across the nest.

Solution. Since the coefficient of heat transfer will be so much bigger on the steam side than on the air side, it can be assumed that the outside surface of the pipes is at the steam temperature, and is therefore constant for all pipes. The mean temperature difference in this case is given by the log mean, and it is unnecessary to use the curves in Fig. 41. Since the ratio of outlet temperature difference to inlet temperature difference is nearly unity, the log mean will be very nearly the same as the arithmetic mean.

That is, mean temperature difference

$$= \frac{(212-60)+(212-85)}{2} = \frac{152+127}{2} = 139 \cdot 5 \text{ F.}°$$

Mean bulk air temperature $= \dfrac{60+85}{2} = 72 \cdot 5°$ F. and mean film temperature $= \dfrac{72 \cdot 5 + 212}{2} = 142°$ F.

Mass velocity at the narrowest section, which is between adjacent tubes of any row,

$$= 8000 \times 3d/(3d-d) = 8000 \times 1 \cdot 5 = 12{,}000 \text{ lb./ft.}^2 \text{ hr.}$$

From Table XVIII, the viscosity of air at $142°$ F. is $0 \cdot 0486$ lb./ft. hr. and

$$Re = \frac{12000}{0 \cdot 0486} \frac{1}{2 \times 12} = 10300.$$

From Table VIII for $X = 1 \cdot 5d$ and $Y = 3d$, for $Re = 10300$

by interpolation $C_H = 1\cdot15$ and $C_f = 1\cdot00$, whence, from expression (66),

$$Hd/k\theta = 0\cdot30\times1\cdot15\times(10300)^{0\cdot6} = 88.$$

The conductivity k of air at $142°$ F. is $0\cdot0162$ B.Th.U./ ft. hr. °F., so that

$$H/\theta = 0\cdot0162\times24\times88 = 34 \text{ B.Th.U./ft.}^2 \text{ hr. °F.}$$

Mass flow of air per 1 ft. length of pipe of any row

$$= 8000\times\left(1\times\frac{1\cdot5}{12}\right) = 1{,}000 \text{ lb./hr.}$$

Specific heat of air $= 0\cdot24$ B.Th.U./lb. °F.

Surface area per foot length of pipe $= \pi/24 = 0\cdot131$ ft.^{2}

Hence, if n is the total number of rows, equating heat transfer from the pipes to heat gained by the air

$$34\times0\cdot131n\times139\cdot5 = 1000\times0\cdot24\times(85-60),$$

whence $n = 9\cdot7$, say 10.

Pressure drop. From expression (67), the pressure drop through the system

$$\Delta p = \frac{C_f\,nM^2_{\max}\times10^{-3}}{\rho(3600)^2}\text{in. of water.}$$

Taking the value of ρ at $72\cdot5°$ F. as $0\cdot075$ lb./ft.^{3}

$$\Delta p = \frac{1\cdot00\times10\times12000^2\times10^{-3}}{0\cdot075\times3600^2} = 1\cdot48 \text{ in. of water.}$$

EXAMPLE 4

Water flowing at 20 gal./min. across a nest of staggered pipes 12 in. long, $\frac{1}{4}$ in. outer diameter, and $0\cdot08$ in. wall thickness, is to be cooled from $180°$ F. (t_1) to $160°$ F. (t_2). The rows consist of 50 and 49 pipes alternately. Air, initially at $50°$ F. (t_1'), is blown through the pipes at 35 ft./sec. Find the number of rows required, and the drop in pressure of the air between inlet and outlet.

Solution. Reference to pp. 116 and 132 will show that the resistance to heat transfer on the water side can be neglected in comparison with that on the air side. Actually the coefficient of heat transfer on the water side is of the order of 700, that on the air side of 12, B.Th.U./ft.^{2} hr. °F. The pipes can thus be assumed to be at the water temperature, and the drop of temperature all on the air side.

The method of approach is first to guess an outlet air temperature, t_2', find the corresponding heat transfer coefficient from pipe to air, α_a. The mean temperature difference θ_m from water to air is then found from Fig. 41, and, since there is no temperature difference from water to pipe, this is also the temperature difference from pipe to air. The heat transfer for any two successive rows (containing $50+49 = 99$ pipes) can thus be found by multiplying $\alpha_a \theta_m$ by the surface area of the two rows of pipes and the number of rows required to cool the stated quantity of water calculated. The mass flow of air for this number of rows is known. Hence the temperature rise of the air for heat equal to that taken from the water can be calculated and compared with the assumed rise. If the difference is significant, a second and more accurate guess can be made and similarly checked.

As a first guess, suppose the mean outlet air temperature $t_2' = 110°$ F. and the mean bulk temperature of the air therefore $= (50+110)/2 = 80°$ F.

From Table XVIII, ρ for air at $50°$ F. $= 0 \cdot 078$ lb./ft.^{3} and μ at $80°$ F. $= 0 \cdot 045$ lb./ft. hr.

Hence $\qquad Re = \dfrac{35 \times 3600 \times 0 \cdot 078 \times 0 \cdot 234}{0 \cdot 045 \times 12} = 4260$

and the flow will therefore be turbulent.

From the curves in Fig. 33, for a mass velocity M

$$= 35 \times 3600 \times 0 \cdot 078 = 9830 \text{ lb./ft.}^2 \text{ hr.},$$

diameter $0 \cdot 234$ in. and temperature $80°$ F.,

$$\alpha_a = 12 \cdot 5 \text{ B.Th.U./ft.}^2 \text{ hr. } °\text{F.}$$

The mean temperature difference θ_m from water to air, which is equal to the mean temperature difference from pipe to air, can now be found from the curves in Fig. 41, from which:

$$P = \frac{t_1 - t_2}{t_1 - t_1'} = \frac{180 - 160}{180 - 50} = 0 \cdot 154,$$

$$Q = \frac{t_2' - t_1'}{t_1 - t_1'} = \frac{110 - 50}{180 - 50} = 0 \cdot 46,$$

and
$$R = \frac{\theta_m}{t_1 - t_1'} = 0 \cdot 66,$$

whence $\theta_m = 0 \cdot 66 \times 130 = 86$ F.$^\circ$

Total rate of heat transfer from water to pipes $= \alpha_a \theta_m S$, where S is the total inside surface area of the pipes.

But this must be equal to the heat lost by the water which, since 1 gallon of water $= 10$ lb., is equal to

$$20 \times 10 \times 60 \times (180-60) = 240{,}000 \text{ B.Th.U./hr.}$$

Hence $S = 240000/12 \cdot 5 \times 86 = 223$ ft.^{2}

Surface area of any two successive rows of pipes

$$= \frac{99 \times \pi \times 0 \cdot 234}{12} = 6 \cdot 06 \text{ ft.}^2$$

Hence the number of rows required $= \dfrac{2 \times 223}{6 \cdot 06} = 74$ and the total surface area $= 224$ ft.^{2}

Cross-sectional area of each pipe

$$= \frac{\pi}{4} \times \left(\frac{0 \cdot 234}{12}\right)^2 = 0 \cdot 00030 \text{ ft.}^2$$

Mass flow of air through 74 rows

$$= 9830 \times 74 \times \frac{99}{2} \times 0 \cdot 00030 = 10{,}800 \text{ lb./hr.}$$

But the temperature rise which would be caused in this by the 240,000 B.Th.U./hr. needed for cooling the water would be $\dfrac{240000}{10800 \times 0 \cdot 24} = 93$ degrees, making the outlet air temperature 143° F. instead of the guessed value of 110° F.

A second and better guess can now be made, by taking t_2 as

$$\frac{143+110}{2} = 126° \text{ F.}$$

This will not affect α_a appreciably and we shall have, from Fig. 41,

$$P = 0 \cdot 154, \qquad Q = \frac{126-50}{130} = 0 \cdot 585, \quad \text{and} \quad R = 0 \cdot 58,$$

whence
$$\theta_m = 0 \cdot 58 \times 130 = 75 \cdot 4 \text{ F.}^\circ$$

and
$$S = \frac{240000}{12 \cdot 5 \times 75 \cdot 4} = 254 \text{ ft.}^2,$$

giving the number of rows required as $\dfrac{254 \times 2}{6 \cdot 06} = 84$.

The outlet air temperature required for the cooling of the water would be $50 + (93 \times 74)/84 = 132°$ F., which is fairly close to the guessed value of $126°$ F. However, it is clear that 84 rows are still not quite enough, and that the correct answer should be about 86 rows, or, in view of the uncertainty of the heat transfer data, say 90 rows to leave a small margin of safety.

Calculation of pressure drop Δp. From expression (33),
$\Delta p = \dfrac{2fl\rho v^2}{gd} = \dfrac{2flM^2}{gd\rho}$. Taking t_2' as $130°$ F., mean temperature

$$= \frac{50 + 130}{2} = 90° \text{ F.}$$

At $90°$ F., $\mu = 0 \cdot 0456$ lb./ft. hr., $\rho = 0 \cdot 072$ lb./ft.^{3}
$$Re = \frac{Md}{\mu} = \frac{9830 \times 0 \cdot 234}{0 \cdot 0456 \times 12} = 4,200.$$

From Fig. 23, f for a smooth pipe $= 0 \cdot 01$,
$$\Delta p = \frac{2 \times 0 \cdot 01 \times 1 \times (9830)^2 \times 12}{4 \cdot 17 \times 10^8 \times 0 \cdot 234 \times 0 \cdot 072} = 3 \cdot 3 \text{ lb./ft.}^2 = 0 \cdot 64 \text{ in. water.}$$

Alternatively the pressure drop could be estimated from the Reynolds analogy, (44), as follows:

Taking ρ at a mean air temperature of $90°$ F., and θ_m as 73 F.$^°$

$$\Delta p = \frac{(9830)^2 (130 - 80)}{0 \cdot 072 \times 4 \cdot 17 \times 10^8 \times 73} = 3 \cdot 5 \text{ lb./ft.}^2 = 0 \cdot 67 \text{ in water.}$$

EXAMPLE 5

A heat exchanger consists of 50 rows of pipes arranged in line, each row containing 10 pipes of $\frac{3}{4}$ in. outside diameter, $0 \cdot 048$ in. wall thickness, and 12 in. length. The centre-to-centre distance between adjacent pipes in a row, Y, $= \frac{15}{16}$ in. ($1 \cdot 25d$), and between adjacent rows, X, $= 1\frac{1}{8}$ in. ($1 \cdot 5d$). The exchanger is used to cool 25 gal./min. of fresh water initially at $t_1 = 210°$ F., passed across the pipes. Sea water initially at $t_1' = 60°$ F. is passed through the pipes at 500 gal./min. Estimate the outlet temperature of the fresh water. The viscosity, density, and thermal conductivity of sea water may be taken as the same as those of fresh water (see Table XVIII).

Solution. The outlet temperatures of both liquids are first guessed, and then, by calculation, it can be found how far they are incompatible, and a second and better guess made and, if necessary, a similar process repeated. Since the mass flow of the sea water is twenty times that of the fresh water, the temperature drop of the fresh water will be twenty times the temperature rise of the sea water. As a first guess, suppose that the outlet temperature t_2 of the fresh water is $100°$ F., making $t_1-t_2 = 110$ F.$°$ Then the outlet temperature of the sea water t_2' will be $65·5°$ F. since $t_2'-t_1' = 110/20 = 5·5$ F.$°$

Flow through pipes. Mean temperature of sea water

$$= (60+65·5)/2 = 62·7° \text{ F.}$$

Total number of pipes $= 500.$ Inside diameter

$$= 0·75-0·096 = 0·654 \text{ in.}$$

Flow area through pipes $= 500 \times \dfrac{\pi}{4} \times \left(\dfrac{0·654}{12}\right)^2 = 1·17$ ft.^{2} Mass flow of sea water $= 500 \times 10 \times 60 = 300,000$ lb./hr. Mass velocity of sea water (inner liquid)

$$= M_i = \frac{300000}{1·17} = 256,000 \text{ lb./ft.}^2 \text{ hr.}$$

Mean temperature of sea water $= (60+65·5)/2 = 62·7°$ F. For water at $62·7°$ F., $\mu = 2·65$ lb./ft. hr.

$$Re_i = M_i\, d/\mu = 256000 \times 0·654/2·65 \times 12 = 5260,$$

which indicates turbulent flow.

From the curves in Fig. 35, for water at $62·7°$ F. flowing at $256,000$ lb./ft.^{2} hr. through a pipe of $0·654$ in. diameter, the heat transfer coefficient $\alpha_i = 315$ B.Th.U./ft.^{2} hr. $°$F.

Flow across pipes. As the pipes are arranged in line the minimum flow area is between the pipes of any row, and the free flow cross-section therefore $= \dfrac{10 \times 3 \times 1}{12 \times 16} = 0·156$ ft.^{2}

Mass flow of fresh water $= 25 \times 10 \times 60 = 15,000$ lb./hr.

Mass velocity of fresh water (outer liquid)

$$= M_0 = \frac{15000}{0 \cdot 156} = 96,000 \text{ lb./ft.}^2 \text{ hr.}$$

Mean temperature of fresh water $= (210+100)/2 = 155°$ F.

The heat transfer coefficient α_0 for cross flow over a bank of pipes is by (65) given by $\alpha_0 \, d/k = 0 \cdot 33 C_H \, Re^{0 \cdot 6} Pr^{0 \cdot 3}$, where c, μ, and k are evaluated at film temperature. The mean pipe-wall temperature must therefore be guessed; as a first guess, suppose it is $(62 \cdot 7 + 155)/2 = 109°$ F. Then the mean film temperature $= (109 + 155)/2 = 132°$ F. For water at $132°$ F., $\mu = 1 \cdot 21$ lb./ft. hr., $Pr = 3 \cdot 25$, $k = 0 \cdot 37$ B.Th.U./ft. hr. °F.

$$Re_0 = M_0 \, d/\mu = \frac{96000 \times 3}{1 \cdot 21 \times 48} = 4960 \quad \text{and} \quad Re^{0 \cdot 6} = 165.$$

From Table VII for $X = 1 \cdot 5d$, $Y = 1 \cdot 25d$, and $Re = 4960$, $C_H = 1 \cdot 05$.

$$\alpha_0 = \frac{0 \cdot 37 \times 48 \times 0 \cdot 33 \times 1 \cdot 05 (4960)^{0 \cdot 6} (3 \cdot 25)^{0 \cdot 3}}{3}$$

$$= 482 \text{ B.Th.U./hr. °F. per ft.}^2 \text{ outer pipe surface}$$

$$= 482 \times \frac{0 \cdot 75}{0 \cdot 654} = 553 \text{ B.Th.U./hr. °F. per ft.}^2 \text{ inner pipe}$$

surface.

The overall coefficient U in B.Th.U./hr. °F. per ft.^{2} inner pipe surface is given by $\dfrac{1}{U} = \dfrac{1}{315} + \dfrac{1}{553} = \dfrac{1}{201}.$

Whence $U = 201$ B.Th.U./hr. °F. per ft.^{2} inner pipe surface.

Using the curves in Fig. 41, to find the mean overall temperature difference,

$$P = \frac{t_1 - t_2}{t_1 - t_1'} = \frac{210 - 100}{210 - 60} = \frac{110}{150} = 0 \cdot 733,$$

$$Q = \frac{t_2' - t_1'}{t_1 - t_1'} = \frac{65 \cdot 5 - 60}{210 - 60} = \frac{5 \cdot 5}{150} = 0 \cdot 037,$$

whence $R = 0 \cdot 54$ and $\theta_m = 0 \cdot 54 \times 150 = 81$ F.°

Total inside surface area of pipes

$$S_i = 500 \times \pi \times 0 \cdot 654/12 = 85 \cdot 5 \text{ ft.}^2$$

Equating the heat transfer to heat taken from fresh water:

$$US_i\,\theta_m = 15000(t_1-t_2), \text{ i.e. } (t_1-t_2) = \frac{201\times 85\cdot 5\times 81}{15000} = 93 \text{ F.}°$$

The original guessed value was 110 F.° A more accurate estimate will be given by $(t_1-t_2) = (93+110)/2 = 101$ F.°, making $t_2 = 109°$ F. and $(t_2'-t_1') = \dfrac{101}{20} = 5$ F.°, making

$$t_2' = 65° \text{ F.}$$

Mean temperature of fresh water

$$= (210+109)/2 = 159° \text{ F. (first guess } 155° \text{ F.).}$$

Mean temperature of sea water

$$= (60+65)/2 = 62\cdot 5° \text{ F. (first guess } 62\cdot 7° \text{ F.).}$$

Mean pipe-wall temperature t_s is given by

$$\alpha_i\!\left(t_s - \frac{t_1'+t_2'}{2}\right) = \alpha_0\!\left(\frac{t_1+t_2}{2} - t_s\right),$$

or $320(t_s-62\cdot 5) = 553(159-t_s)$, whence

$$t_s = \frac{(553\times 159)+(320\times 62\cdot 5)}{320+553} = \frac{107900}{873} = 124° \text{ F.}$$

(first guess 109° F.).

Since the outside coefficients vary only slowly with absolute temperature, it is clear that the above changes will not alter the value of U by more than a few per cent.

Again referring to Fig. 41,

$$P = \frac{210-109}{210-60} = \frac{101}{150} = 0\cdot 67, \qquad Q = \frac{5}{150} = 0\cdot 033,$$

whence $R = 0\cdot 58$, and $\theta_m = 0\cdot 58\times 150 = 87$ F.°

$$(t_1-t_2) = \frac{201\times 85\cdot 5\times 87}{15000} = 100 \text{ F.}°,$$

which compares favourably with the second guess of 101 F.° The outlet temperature of fresh water will therefore be 109° F.

BIBLIOGRAPHY

FORCED CONVECTION

1. COLBURN, A. P., DREW, T. B., and WORTHINGTON, H. 'Heat Transfer to a 3–1 Hydrogen-Nitrogen Mixture at High Pressures.' *Ind. Eng. Chem.* 1947, **39**, 958.

2. GRAETZ, L. *Z. Math. Physik*, 1880, **25**, 316, 375; *Ann. Physik*, 1883, **18**, 79 and 1885, **25**, 337.

3. NUSSELT, W. 'Der Wärmeübergang in Röhrleitungen.' *Z.V.d.I.* 1909, **53**, 1750 and 1808. Also 'Die Abhängigkeit der Wärmeübergangzahl von der Rohrlänge.' Ibid. 1910, **54**, 1154.

4. LÉVÊQUE, M. A. 'Les Lois de la transmission de la chaleur par convection.' *Ann. des Mines*, 1928, **13**, 201, 305, 381. See also Drew, T. B., 'Mathematical Attacks on Forced Convection Problems', *Trans. Am. Inst. Chem. Eng.* 1931, **26**, 26; Goldstein, S., *Modern Developments in Fluid Dynamics* (Clarendon Press, 1938), vol. ii, Chap. XIV.

5. SIEDER, E. N., and TATE, G. E. 'Heat Transfer and Pressure Drop of Liquids in Tubes.' *Ind. Eng. Chem.* 1936, **28**, 1429.

6. BOUSSINESQ, J. 'Sur la manière dont les vitesses, dans un tube cylindrique, se distribuent jusqu'aux endroits où se trouve établi un régime uniforme.' *Comptes rendus*, 1891, **113**, 9. Also 'Calcul de la moindre longueur que doit avoir un tube circulaire, pour qu'un régime sensiblement uniforme s'y établisse.' Ibid. p. 49.

7. COLBURN, A. P. 'Correlation of Heating and Cooling Data for Flow through Tubes.' *Trans. Am. Inst. Chem. Eng.* 1933, **29**, 174.

8. COPE, W. F. 'Friction and Heat Transfer Coefficients.' *Proc. Inst. Mech. Eng.* 1937, **137**, 165.

9. WASHINGTON, L., and MARKS, W. M. 'Heat Transfer and Pressure Drop in Rectangular Air Passages.' *Ind. Eng. Chem.* 1937, **29**, 337.

10. DAVIS, A. H. 'Convective Cooling in Liquids.' *Phil. Mag.* 1922, **44**, 920 and 1924, **47**, 1057.

11. —— 'The Cooling Power of a Stream of Very Viscous Liquid.' Ibid. 1925, **49**, 285.

12. PIRET, E. L., JAMES, W., and STACEY, M. 'Heat Transmission from Fine Wires to Water.' *Ind. Eng. Chem.* 1947, **39**, 1098.

13. HILPERT, R. 'Wärmeabgabe von geheizten Drähten und Rohren.' *Forsch. Gebiete Ingenieurwes.* 1933, **4**, 215.

14. HUGE, E. C. 'Experimental Investigation of Effects of Equipment Size on Convection Heat Transfer and Flow Resistance in Cross Flow of Gases over Tube Banks.' *Trans. Am. Soc. Mech. Eng.* 1937, **59**, Pro–59–7, 573.

15. PIERSON, O. L. 'Experimental Investigation of Influence of Tube Arrangement on Convection Heat Transfer and Flow Resistance in Cross Flow of Gases over Tube Banks.' Ibid. 1937, **59**, Pro–59–6, 563.

16. GRIMISON, E. D. 'Correlation and Utilization of New Data on Flow

Resistance and Heat Transfer for Cross Flow of Gases over Tube Banks.' Ibid. 1937, **59**, 583.

17. KUZNETZOFF, N. V., and LOKSHIN, V. A. 'Convectional Heat Transfer for the Cross Flow of a Fluid over Tube Banks.' *Teplo i Sila*, 1937, **13**, No. 10, 19.

18. LOKSHIN, V. A. 'Influence of Angle of Impingement upon Heat Transfer in Tube Bundles.' Ibid. 1940, **16**, No. 8, 29.

19. ORNATSKI, A. P. 'Heat Transfer in Tube Bundles as a Function of the Angle of Impingement.' *Sovetskoe Kotloturbostroenie*, 1940, No. 2, p. 48.

20. COLBURN, A. P. 'Heat Transfer by Natural and Forced Convection.' *Eng. Bull., Purdue University*, 1942, **26**, No. 1, Bull. No. 84.

21. JAKOB, M., and DOW, W. M. 'Heat Transfer from a Cylindrical Surface to Air in Parallel Flow etc.' *Trans. Am. Soc. Mech. Eng.* 1946, **68**, 123.

22. Unpublished work done at the Imperial College of Science and Technology.

23. FAGE, A., and FAULKNER, V. M. *On the Relation between Heat Transfer and Surface Friction for Laminar Flow.* A.R.C.T. 3060, F.M. 31. See also A.R.C.T. 2997, F.M. 16 (1930); Brit. Adv. Committee Aero. Rep. and Mem. No. 1408, 1931.

24. See MCADAMS, *Heat Transmission* (McGraw-Hill, 1942), 237.

25. SMITH, D. M. 'Mean Temperature-difference in Cross Flow.' *Engineering*, 1934, **138**, 479 and 606.

26. Symposium on Finned Surfaces. *Trans. Am. Soc. Mech. Eng.* 1945, **67**, 601–702.

27. MCADAMS, W. H., NICOLAI, L. A., and KEENAN, J. H. 'Measurements of Recovery Factors and Coefficients of Heat Transfer in a Tube for Subsonic Flow of Air.' *Trans. Am. Inst. Chem. Eng.* 1946, **42**, 907.

VII

HEAT TRANSFER FROM CONDENSING VAPOURS

FILM CONDENSATION OF PURE VAPOUR

Streamline flow. When either a saturated or a superheated vapour comes into contact with a surface kept at a temperature below the condensing point, vapour condenses on the surface, imparting to it its latent heat. If the cooling surface is wettable, the condensate forms a continuous liquid film, which, with gravity acting against viscosity, runs down the surface. The heat transferred to the surface must thus pass by conduction through the condensate layer, the thickness δ of which depends upon both the rate of condensation and the rate at which the surface can drain under the action of gravity. Nusselt [1], in 1916, showed that in such a case, in the steady state, when a balance has been established between the rate of condensation and the rate of draining, the heat transfer for a pure saturated vapour can be calculated for simple geometrical arrangements, provided the flow of the condensate down the surface is laminar. He assumed that the temperature of the surface of the film in contact with the wall is at the wall temperature, and uniform; and that the temperature of the surface of the film in contact with the vapour is at the saturation temperature. Actually, of course, there must be some temperature drop, however small, from vapour to condensate film, otherwise no condensation would occur, but it can usually be neglected compared with the temperature drop across the film.

As we shall see later, under certain conditions a vapour may condense not as a continuous film, but as separate droplets, giving a vastly increased rate of heat transfer; and it must be borne clearly in mind that the results given in this section apply to film condensation only.

The results obtained by Nusselt for the average heat transfer coefficient, α, over the whole surface, give, for the condensation of a pure saturated vapour on a vertical plane or a vertical tube:

$$\alpha = \frac{H}{\theta} = 0.94 \left(\frac{q\rho^2 k^3 g}{\mu h \theta}\right)^{\frac{1}{4}} \text{B.Th.U./ft.}^2 \text{ hr. }°\text{F.}, \qquad (84)$$

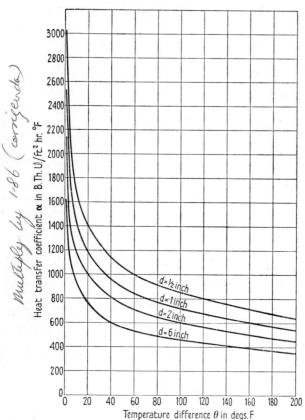

Fig. 42. Heat transfer coefficients for saturated steam condensing at 212° F. on horizontal cylinders.

or, if the surface is inclined at an angle of ϕ to the vertical, $(\cos \phi)^{\frac{1}{4}}$ times the above expression.

For horizontal tubes:

$$\alpha = \frac{H}{\theta} = 0.72 \left(\frac{q\rho^2 k^3 g}{\mu d \theta}\right)^{\frac{1}{4}} \text{B.Th.U./ft.}^2 \text{ hr. }°\text{F.} \qquad (85)$$

According to the Nusselt expressions, the heat transfer

coefficients for streamline flow of the condensate should decrease with increase of θ, and should be less for a horizontal cylinder of diameter d than for a vertical cylinder of height $h = d$. For the more usual practical case of a cylinder long compared with its

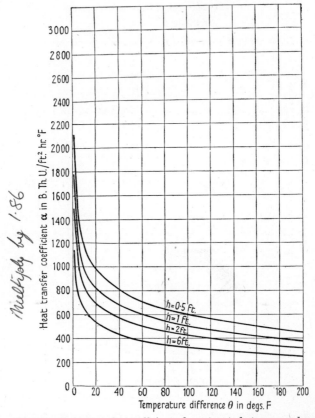

Fig. 43. Heat transfer coefficients for saturated steam condensing at 212° F. on vertical cylinders or vertical planes.

diameter, α should be less in the vertical position than in the horizontal position.

Figs. 42 and 43 show the coefficients of heat transfer, as calculated from these expressions, for air-free saturated steam, condensing at atmospheric pressure on vertical surfaces of heights $\frac{1}{2}$, 1, 2, and 6 ft., and on horizontal cylinders of diameters

Multiply by 1·86

mult. values by $12^{\frac{1}{4}} = 1.86$ (Corrigenda)

$\frac{1}{2}$, 1, 2, and 6 in., for temperature differences up to 200 F.°
between steam saturation temperature and surface temperature.
It will be seen that for the bigger temperature differences
the coefficients are of the order of about 300 to 800 B.Th.U./
ft.² hr. °F., and that for the smaller temperature differences
they go up to several thousand B.Th.U./ft.² hr. °F. No general
comparison of these condensation coefficients with the coefficients of heat transfer by natural convection from a gas to a
surface can be given, since the condensing steam coefficients
decrease with increasing θ while the natural convection coefficients increase with increasing θ, but it is useful to note that
the condensing steam coefficients are of the order of 1,000 times
the gas coefficients. They are 10 to 100 times the forced convection gas coefficients according to the speed and geometrical
conditions. If therefore a gas on one side of a metal partition
is being heated by steam condensing on the other side, the
resistance to heat flow on the steam side can be assumed almost
negligible compared with that on the gas side. The metal will
consequently be almost at the steam temperature.

Close approximations to the Nusselt values of α for film condensation are given by

$$\alpha = \frac{b_1}{h^{\frac{1}{4}}\theta^{\frac{1}{4}}} \text{ B.Th.U./ft.² hr. °F.}$$

for a vertical surface of height h feet,   (86)

or $\alpha = \frac{b_2}{d^{\frac{1}{4}}\theta^{\frac{1}{4}}} \text{ B.Th.U./ft.² hr. °F.}$

for a horizontal pipe of diameter d feet,   (87)

where b_1 and b_2 are constants depending on the vapour. Some
values of b_1 and b_2 for saturated steam are given in the table
below.

TABLE XI. *Constants for Use in Expressions* (86) *and* (87)

Steam pressure	Steam temp. °F.	b_1	b_2	Range of θ F.°
Atmospheric . .	212	4,000	3,100	0–200
0·95 lb./in.² abs. .	100	3,000	2,300	0–90

The Nusselt expressions can be written in the dimensionless form:

$$\frac{H}{\theta}\left(\frac{\mu^2}{k^3\rho^2 g}\right)^{\frac{1}{3}} = \text{constant}(Re)^{-\frac{1}{3}} = \text{constant}\left(\frac{4M_l}{\mu}\right)^{-\frac{1}{3}}, \qquad (88)$$

where the constant is 1·47 for vertical, and 1·50 for horizontal· pipes, and M_l is the mass rate of flow of the condensate from the lowest point of the surface, per unit breadth of surface, in lb./hr./ft. For a vertical tube $M_l = w/\pi d$, where w is the total mass rate of flow of the condensate from the lowest point on the condensing surface in lb./hr. For a horizontal tube $M_l = w/l$, where l is the length of the tube.

Effect of turbulence. It has been pointed out that at high rates of heat transfer to tall vertical surfaces the motion of the condensate along the lower parts of the surface may become turbulent. The critical velocity is given by:

$$Re = \frac{4v\rho\delta}{\mu} = \frac{4M_l}{\mu} = 2100. \qquad (89)$$

For horizontal tubes the critical velocity is given by

$$\frac{4v\rho\delta}{\mu} = \frac{2M_l}{\mu} = 2100, \qquad (90)$$

but, since in this case the condensing height is usually inherently small, turbulence is not likely to occur.

Kirkbride [2], for data of Badger, Monrad, and Diamond [3] on the condensation of diphenyl vapour on vertical nickel pipes at Reynolds numbers above the critical value, and Badger [4] condensing Dowtherm A, found good agreement with the empirical dimensionless equation, based on the mean coefficient for the whole pipe:

$$\frac{H}{\theta}\left(\frac{\mu^2}{k^3\rho^2 g}\right)^{\frac{1}{3}} = 0\cdot 0077\left(\frac{4M_l}{\mu}\right)^{\frac{2}{5}}. \qquad (91)$$

Tentative theoretical relations derived by Colburn [5] agree fairly well with the experimental results. The theoretical relations for both streamline and turbulent flow are shown in Fig. 44, which also gives Kirkbride's results for comparison. It will be seen from Fig. 44 that, whereas for streamline flow of the condensate the heat transfer coefficient decreases with increasing θ, as shown by the downward slant of the curve with increasing rate of condensation, for turbulent flow it increases, as shown by the upward slant of the curve with increasing rate of condensation.

Even when Re is below the critical value, and the flow is not turbulent, ripples may form in the lower parts of the condensate

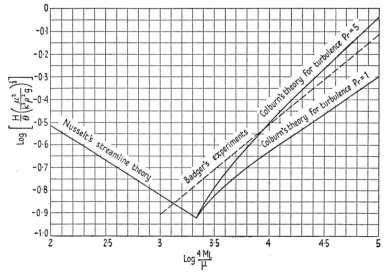

FIG. 44. Dimensionless correlation of theoretical and experimental results for film condensation of a pure vapour on a vertical cylinder or vertical plane.

stream, causing the thickness to be alternately above and below the average. This increases the rate of heat transfer, since the average value of k/δ is higher than when no ripples form and δ, except for a slow gradual change from top to bottom of the surface, is constant.

Experimental results and practical formulae. Many measurements have been made of the heat transfer from steam and other pure vapours condensing on both horizontal and vertical surfaces; but unfortunately even in the cases where the condensation was known to be mainly filmwise, there is not always certainty of complete freedom from drop formation. However, the results for condensation on the outside of horizontal tubes show fair agreement with (85), although on the whole there is a tendency for the measured results to be high. Most of them lie between 20 per cent. above and 10 per cent. below the calculated ones, although the deviation in a few cases is greater than this.

For vertical surfaces the experimental data are consistently above the Nusselt values, and, even for streamline flow of the condensate, the constant in (84) should usually be increased by at least 20 to 25 per cent. When Re is above 2,100, and the flow of the condensate has become turbulent, the Kirkbride expression (91) may be used. Indeed, turbulence may set in at lower Reynolds numbers, even at 1,600 or below.

For a vertical tier of n horizontal tubes, McAdams recommends using the Nusselt relation:

$$\frac{H}{\theta} = 0 \cdot 72 \left(\frac{k^3 \rho^2 g q}{n d \mu \theta} \right)^{\frac{1}{4}} = 0 \cdot 95 \left(\frac{k^3 \rho^2 g l}{\mu w} \right)^{\frac{1}{3}} \tag{92}$$

according to whether it is more convenient to estimate θ or M_l. But considering that this makes no allowance for possible turbulence of the film caused by high vapour velocity, or for splashing of the condensate, it would probably be advisable to add 10 to 20 per cent., even when there is no drop formation.

Effect of vapour velocity. If the vapour flows at high velocity over the condensing surface the rate of heat transfer may be appreciably modified. Vapour flowing upwards in a vertical tube would tend to increase the thickness of the condensate film, and so decrease the rate of heat transfer, but, as Nusselt showed, for downward flow of vapour in a vertical tube, H/θ should increase as the velocity increases. Jakob [6] extended Nusselt's calculations to take account of the continuous decrease in the steam velocity with distance along the tube, which may be considerable at high rates of heat transfer. The resulting differential equation is very complex, but the solution for a 4-ft. tube agreed well with experiment, the coefficients of heat transfer for a steam velocity of 250 ft. per second being roughly double those for a very slow flow.

Effect of air in steam. It is well known that even small proportions of non-condensable gas may seriously reduce the rate of heat transfer from a condensing vapour. The non-condensable gas tends to collect on the surface of the condensate layer, forming a layer of a mixture of non-condensable gas and vapour in which the vapour pressure is lower than in the main body of the enclosure. To reach the surface of the condensate layer, the vapour from the main body must therefore pass by diffusion through the mixture layer. The resistance offered by the gas layer becomes more serious as the proportion of non-condensable gas increases and as the flow velocity decreases. It has thus been suggested that in tubular condensers the cross-sectional area of the steam space should be reduced near the end of the path so as to maintain a high flow velocity. The effect of the gas depends upon the other resistances to the heat flow, and exact solutions of heat transfer problems from mixtures of vapour and non-condensing gases are not usually possible since composition, velocity, and temperature vary along the path. But Colburn and Hougen [7] have published a detailed study of the effect of air in steam, considered as a dehumidification problem, and have attempted a solution for a tubular cooler condenser [8] to which the reader is referred. Their method was to equate the heat transfer to the surface of the condensate film to the heat passing through the condensate film and wall to the cooling water.

Dropwise Condensation of Pure Vapour

When a cooling surface is smooth and greasy, vapour may condense either partially or wholly in the form of separate drops of liquid. Thus, a proportion of the surface is exposed directly or nearly directly to the vapour, with greatly increased heat transfer; and the heat transfer even to the drops of liquid is large compared with that to a plane layer of the same mean thickness. Moreover, the condensate on a vertical or inclined surface runs down more quickly than does a film, since the drops as they roll down the surface coalesce with other drops and carry them down too.

Thus, although for film condensation the results usually agree reasonably well with theory, for dropwise condensation they may be up to 8 or 10 times as high; and until this was realized it was not found possible to explain the wide discrepancies in the results of different workers for apparently similar conditions.

Much attention has been given to the possibility of maintaining dropwise condensation on cooling surfaces, and so keeping up an increased rate of heat transfer. Drew and his colleagues in the U.S.A., after examining their own and other observations, came to the conclusion that clean steam, whether or not it contains non-condensable gases, always condenses in a film on clean surfaces, rough or polished, dropwise condensation being found only if the surface is contaminated in certain ways. Film condensation, however, is more easy to maintain on rough surfaces, drop condensation on smooth surfaces.

Although many substances while actually on a surface will make it non-wettable, and so prevent a film of liquid from spreading over it, only those that are strongly adsorbed or otherwise firmly held are significant as drop promoters in a condenser. Some contaminants seem to depend for their activity as drop promoters on the amount of non-condensable gas present; some are specifically effective on certain metals, e.g. mercaptans on copper alloys; while others, such as the fatty acids, are generally effective. Neither mild steel nor aluminium will give dropwise condensation, except temporarily. For further details the reader is referred to a review by Drew, Hottel, and McAdams [9].

Effect of surface tension. Kirkbride [2], by comparing the condensation of gasoline with that of steam and aniline, on smooth glass tubes, found that the form which the condensate takes depends upon both the surface tension and the rate of condensation. At the lower rates, steam and aniline, owing to their high surface tension, condensed in drops, but gasoline with a much lower surface tension gave a film. By increasing the condensation rates of steam and aniline, however, they also could be made to condense as films. In industrial plant the condensation is probably usually filmwise, because of the high rates of condensation and the comparative roughness of ordinary industrial surfaces; but both types of condensation may occur, either on different parts of a surface, or at different times, especially if the

surface is liable to be greasy, and the changes sometimes give rise
to results which may appear anomalous.

HEAT TRANSFER FROM A SUPERHEATED VAPOUR

If the temperature of a condensing surface is below the vapour
saturation temperature, the heat transfer rates for any given
difference between vapour saturation temperature and condensing surface temperature are practically the same for superheated as for saturated steam, except when this temperature
difference is so small that the sensible heat transfer is comparable
with the latent heat transfer. If the surface temperature is above
the saturation temperature the rate of heat transfer for a superheated vapour must be calculated from the appropriate convection formulae for a gas, in this case, of course, taking the
actual temperature difference between vapour and surface.
Even when convection is high enough to keep the surface temperature at the inlet end of a heat exchanger above the saturation
temperature, condensation may begin farther along the exchanger. In such cases a preliminary estimate of the point at
which the surface temperature reaches the saturation value must
be made.

EXAMPLE 1

It is required to condense 10,000 lb. of steam per hour, at
212° F., on a bank of pipes through which cooling water flows at
6 ft./sec. If the water enters at 50° F. and leaves at 100° F., how
long should each pipe be, and how many would be needed? Both
inner and outer pipe diameters may be taken as 1 in., and the
coefficients of heat transfer on the water and steam sides as 800
and 1,000 B.Th.U./ft.² hr. °F. respectively. Latent heat of
steam at 212° F. = 970 B.Th.U./lb.

Solution. Heat per pipe given to water $= v\rho c \Delta t \times$ cross-
sectional area of pipe

$$= 6 \times 60 \times 60 \times 62 \times 1 \times (100-50) \times \frac{\pi}{4 \times 12 \times 12}$$

$$= 364{,}000 \text{ B.Th.U./hr.}$$

Heat required to condense steam $= 10000 \times 970$

$$= 9{,}700{,}000 \text{ B.Th.U./hr.}$$

So number of pipes required = $(10000 \times 970)/364000 = 26 \cdot 6$, say 27.

Coefficient of heat transfer, steam to water

$$= \frac{1}{(1/800+1/1000)} = 444 \text{ B.Th.U./ft.}^2 \text{ hr. }^\circ\text{F.}$$

Mean θ, steam to water $= 212 - \dfrac{50+100}{2} = 137 \text{ F.}^\circ$

Heat transfer $= 444 \times 137 = 60{,}800 \text{ B.Th.U./ft.}^2 \text{ hr.}$

Area of pipe required $= (10000 \times 970)/60800 = 159 \text{ ft.}^2$

Surface area per ft. length $= \pi d = 22/(7 \times 12) \text{ ft.}^2$

Total length needed $= (159 \times 7 \times 12)/22 = 606 \text{ ft.}$

Length per pipe $= 606/27 = 22 \cdot 4 \text{ ft.}$

EXAMPLE 2

Dry saturated steam at 212° F. is condensing on the outside of a bank of pipes in which each row consists of 20 horizontal pipes, each 3 ft. long, one above the other. If the temperature of the outer surface of the pipes is 198° F., what will be the weight of condensate per row? Outer pipe diameter = 1 in.

Solution. Provided $2M_l/\mu$ is less than 2100, as it usually would be for horizontal pipes, and the condensation filmwise, (92) will be reasonably applicable (see p. 168). Since θ, and not w, is known, the form to use is

$$H = 0 \cdot 72\theta \left(\frac{k^3 \rho^2 gq}{nd\mu\theta} \right)^{\frac{1}{4}}.$$

For a film temperature of $\dfrac{212+198}{2} = 205^\circ$ F.

$$H = 0 \cdot 72 \times (212-198) \times \left(\frac{0 \cdot 391^3 \times 60 \cdot 4^2 \times 4 \cdot 17 \times 10^8 \times 970}{20 \times 1/12 \times 0 \cdot 705 \times 14} \right)^{\frac{1}{4}}$$
$$= 15{,}300 \text{ B.Th.U./ft.}^2 \text{ hr.}$$

Hence $w = \dfrac{15300 \times 20\pi dl}{q} = 248 \text{ lb./hr.}$

It must now be verified that the flow is non-turbulent by working out

$$2M_l/\mu = 2w/\mu l = 2 \times 248/0 \cdot 705 \times 3 = 234;$$

this is far below the critical value of 2,100. Nevertheless, as already explained, the value obtained for w is likely to be low, since any degree of dropwise condensation, splashing of condensate, or turbulence induced by high vapour velocity, would tend to increase it.

BIBLIOGRAPHY

CONDENSATION

1. NUSSELT, W. 'Die Oberflächenkondensation des Wasserdampfes.' *Z.V.d.I.* 1916, **60**, 541, 569.
2. KIRKBRIDE, C. G. 'Heat Transfer by Condensing Vapour on Vertical Tubes.' *Ind. Eng. Chem.* 1934, **26**, 425; *Trans. Am. Inst. Chem. Eng.* 1933–4, **30**, 170.
3. BADGER, W. L., MONRAD, C. C., and DIAMOND, H. W. 'The Evaporation of Caustic Soda to High Concentrations by Means of Diphenyl Vapour.' *Ind. Eng. Chem.* 1930, **22**, 700.
4. —— 'Heat Transfer Coefficients for Condensing Dowtherm Films.' Ibid. 1937, **29**, 910.
5. COLBURN, A. P. 'Calculation of Condensation with a Portion of the Condensate Layer in Turbulent Motion.' Ibid. 1934, **26**, 432.
6. JAKOB, M. 'Heat Transfer in Evaporation and Condensation.' *Mechanical Engineering*, 1936, **58**, 643, 729.
7. COLBURN, A. P., and HOUGEN, O. A. 'Studies in Heat Transmission.' *Ind. Eng. Chem.* 1930, **22**, 525.
8. —— —— 'Design of Cooler Condenser for Mixtures of Vapours with Non-condensable Gases.' Ibid. 1934, **26**, 1178.
9. DREW, T. B., HOTTEL, H. C., and McADAMS, W. H. 'Condensation of Vapours.' *Trans. Am. Inst. Chem. Eng.* 1936, **32**, 271.

VIII

HEAT TRANSFER TO BOILING LIQUIDS

IT is convenient, in dealing with boiling liquids, to consider separately the case of liquids boiling on the outside of submerged tubes or other submerged surfaces, where the circulation is usually natural, and that of liquids boiling inside the tubes of evaporators, where the circulation is often forced.

BOILING ON SUBMERGED SURFACES

It is for a number of reasons extremely difficult to measure accurately the heat transfer coefficients from a submerged heated surface to a liquid boiling on it, or even to get consistent results in repeat experiments. This is partly because the rate of heat transfer for any given temperature difference varies widely with the condition of the surface, which affects the ease with which the vapour bubbles are detached. It is partly also because, when a liquid is boiling vigorously, the rate of heat transfer may be so high that there are appreciable temperature gradients, even through the thickness of a metal wall. Moreover, since the columns of bubbles do not rise evenly from the entire surface, but originate in local spots, the rate of heat transfer, and therefore the temperature of the surface, may vary from place to place. These variations make accurate determinations of the temperature difference between surface and liquid almost impossible. Further uncertainties may be caused by the formation of scale, which, at high rates of heat transfer, may greatly reduce the temperature drop from surface to liquid and the rate of boiling, yet may increase the actual heat transfer coefficient on the boiling side because it helps the bubbles to get away freely. It is thus not surprising that our knowledge of heat transfer to boiling liquids is still incomplete, and that really satisfactory correlation of the results, in terms of the physical constants involved, has not been achieved, although several attempts have been made.

The heat transfer coefficient to a boiling liquid depends upon how fast the liquid is boiling, which itself depends upon the temperature difference between the heated surface and the liquid boiling on it. While the liquid is being heated up to boiling-point, the heat transfer of course follows the ordinary laws of convection; but Jakob [1] has shown further that, if the temperature difference between surface and liquid is so small that $(Gr\ Pr)$ is less than 10^9, even after the boiling-point has been reached the stirring effect of the bubbles is negligible compared with convectional motion, and the laws of natural convection hold good. For a vertical surface he found that the expression for streamline flow convection, i.e. $Nu = \text{constant} \times (Gr\ Pr)^{\frac{1}{4}}$, applied, although the appropriate constant, 0·61, was slightly above the mean value of 0·56 in expression (47): this difference is, however, scarcely significant. For a horizontal surface the expression for turbulent natural convection was found to hold, i.e. $Nu = 0·16(Gr\ Pr)^{\frac{1}{3}}$, which agrees closely with Saunders's expression (46) for natural convection to non-boiling water in the turbulent region.

In Jakob's experiments the temperature difference between heated surface and boiling liquid corresponding to $(Gr\ Pr) = 10^9$ was about 3 F.° for the vertical surface and about 10 F.° for the smaller horizontal surface. Much bigger differences would ordinarily be used in industrial appliances.

If the heat input, and consequently the temperature difference, θ, is increased, chains of vapour bubbles rise in increasing quantity through the liquid, their sweeping and stirring action causing the heat transfer to be much above that due to natural convection. When the liquid is stirred in this way by the bubbles, the process is sometimes known as 'nucleate' boiling, and so long as this type of boiling persists, the bigger θ, and thus the more violent the boiling, the bigger the heat transfer coefficient also becomes. But if θ is increased beyond a certain value, the formation of vapour ultimately becomes so rapid that the bubbles cannot get away quickly enough, but tend to merge and spread out over the heating surface in a continuous layer through which the heat has to be transferred by conduction. As a result there is a sharp drop in the heat transfer coefficient, so much so that beyond a certain critical temperature difference, which varies with the conditions, what is known as 'film' boiling sets in, and the actual rate of evaporation decreases with increase of temperature difference. It is clearly of importance in evaporation processes not to push the temperature difference beyond this point.

Effect of geometrical conditions. Neither shape, size, nor inclination seems to have much effect upon the rate of heat transfer to a liquid boiling on a submerged surface, in the range of temperature difference beyond that in which the laws of natural convection apply. Jakob [1], for instance, found that for water and carbon tetrachloride the rate of heat transfer for any given temperature difference was the same whether boiling took place on a vertical cylinder of diameter 1·4 in. or on a horizontal disk of diameter 3·9 in. Further, the heat transfer coefficient varied little with the dimensions of the vessels, or with the depth of liquid down to 2 in., but for depths less than 2 in. there was a rapid increase with decreasing depth. Kaiser [2] in a brew kettle about 2,000 times the size of Jakob's horizontal surface found nearly the same coefficients, while Nukiyama's [3] results for water boiling on an electrically heated platinum wire of diameter 0·005 in. were much the same as those of other observers for cylinders several inches in diameter.

Again, Abbott and Comley [4], testing a model evaporator with nearly sixty horizontal tubes found results agreeing with those for experiments on single tubes; and increasing the clearance between their tubes from ½ in. to 1 in. had practically no effect. The results can thus all be considered together.

Rates of heat transfer for liquids boiling on submerged surfaces. Fig. 45 shows a mean curve based on a number of independent experiments for water boiling at 212° F. on submerged metal surfaces, both the heat transfer coefficient, α, in B.Th.U./ft.² hr °F., and the heat flux, H, in B.Th.U./ft.² hr., from metal to water, being plotted against the corresponding temperature difference. There is considerable divergence between the results of the different experiments upon which Fig. 45 is based, both in the absolute values of α and H and in the slope of the rising portion of the curve, and the values must be considered as approximate only.

At a temperature difference of about 35–40 F.° between metal
and boiling water, but varying a good deal with the conditions,
α reaches its maximum value of about 9,000 B.Th.U./ft.² hr. °F.
The critical temperature difference corresponding to the maxi-

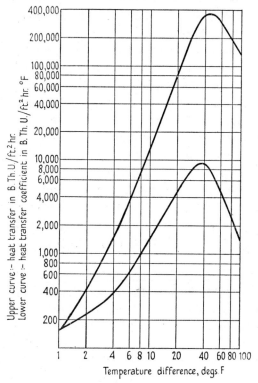

Fig. 45. Heat flux, and heat transfer coefficient, for water boiling
at 212° F. on submerged surfaces.

mum flux of heat is a few degrees above this, say about 40–45° F.
The maximum flux for water boiling at 212° F. under laboratory
conditions is about 350,000 to 400,000 B.Th.U./ft.² hr., depending upon the nature and condition of the surface.

Effect of nature of liquid. For such organic liquids as have
been investigated, both the heat transfer coefficient and the
maximum flux of heat are, at any given pressure, considerably
less than for water, the critical temperature difference being some

20 degrees more than for water. There are wide variations in the results, but for ethyl alcohol boiling on a clean surface a maximum flux of 200,000 B.Th.U./ft.² hr. has been obtained, corresponding values for benzene, butanol, ethanol, methanol, propanol, n-heptane, n-pentane, etc., being 50,000 to 120,000 B.Th.U./ft.² hr., according to the liquid and the nature and condition of the heating surface.

It is obviously important in industrial plant not to exceed the critical temperature difference, and, when dealing with low boiling-point organic liquids, if exhaust steam is used as the heating medium it may be advisable to condense it under reduced pressure. Sauer and Cooper [5] boiling ethyl acetate on a horizontal tube found that with a gauge pressure of 40 lb./in.² the overall heat transfer was only 14 per cent. of that with 12 lb./in.², and 22 per cent. of that with 2 lb./in.²

Effect of condition of surface and surface tension of liquid. The nature and condition of the heating surface and the surface tension at the interface between the boiling liquid and the heating surface have a marked effect upon the rate of heat transfer for any given temperature difference, and also upon the maximum flux and critical temperature difference. This is because, on a non-wettable surface, the vapour bubbles tend to spread out, thus reducing the area of contact between heating surface and liquid, where the rate of heat transfer is much higher than from surface to vapour. Jakob [1] compared the behaviour of a non-wettable surface covered with a thin layer of oil, a partially wettable polished chromium surface, and a specially prepared 'screen' surface, with cubical cavities of linear dimensions and spacings about 0·01 in. which became fully wetted. Three typical shapes of steam bubbles were observed, as shown in Fig. 46. On the non-wettable surface the bubbles (*a*) spread out sideways, their free edges being drawn out into a wedge between the water and the heating surface, which resisted the action of buoyancy. On the smooth chromium-plated surface the bubbles (*b*) rose in columns from a few local spots, irregularly distributed, the number of points of origin increasing with increasing heat input. On the 'screen' surface, roughness so acted against

surface tension that the plate became completely wetted, globu-
lar or oval bubbles with only point contact leaving the surface
while still very small.

Jakob [1] also found that there was a progressive change in the
heat transfer coefficient on the boiling side, which decreased with
the time the heating surface had remained under water, although
after very long immersion, and long period of boiling, a stable
value of the coefficient appeared to be reached. The explanation

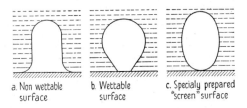

a. Non wettable   b. Wettable   c. Specialy prepared
   surface   surface   "screen" surface

FIG. 46. Formation of steam bubbles.

was thought to be the gradual loss from the plate of adsorbed
air, which provided microcells aiding bubble formation.

Adding agents to reduce the surface tension of the liquid may
greatly increase the heat transfer, the proportional increase
depending largely upon the heat input. Thus, Jakob [1] at a low
input (13,000 B.Th.U./ft.^{2} hr.) found that the addition of 0·5
per cent. of a suitable organic substance to water increased the
heat transfer coefficient by 23 per cent., while Rhodes and
Bridges [6], at a heat input so high that film boiling had been
established, found that the addition of a small quantity of sodium
carbonate increased the coefficient more than ten times, with a
sudden transition to nucleate boiling.

Dimensionless correlation of heat transfer. Many
attempts have been made to obtain more systematic correlations
of boiling heat transfer coefficients with the physical constants
of the liquids concerned. The most important resulting expressions are probably those of Insinger and Bliss [7] and of Jakob
[8], of which the former seems to fit the experimental results
rather better. On account of the possible variations due to
variations in surface condition already discussed, however,

actual values may depart widely from calculated ones. Insinger and Bliss's expression, which is dimensionless, and was derived from their experiments on various liquids boiling on a vertical tube, is

$$\log y = 0.363 + 0.923 \log x - 0.047 (\log x)^2, \qquad (93)$$

where

$$y = \frac{H}{\theta} \left\{ \frac{\rho_v \sigma}{ck\rho_l^3 \sqrt{(q^3 J^3 g)}} \right\}^{0.5} \times 10^{10}$$

and

$$x = H / \{ \rho_l \sqrt{(q^3 J g)} \} \times 10^{10}.$$

It is not applicable either for temperature differences so small that the heat transfer takes place according to the laws of natural convection, or so big that the critical point has been exceeded, and film boiling has consequently set in.

In the above expressions, if H is expressed in B.Th.U./ft.^{2} hr., σ is the surface tension of the boiling liquid in lb./ft., ρ_v and ρ_l the density of vapour and liquid respectively, in lb./ft.^{3}, J the mechanical equivalent of heat, equal to 778 ft. lb./B.Th.U., and q the latent heat of vaporization in B.Th.U./lb. The other symbols bear the same meanings as previously.

Equation (93) means that the heat transfer coefficient is approximately proportional to $c^{0.5}$, $k^{0.5}$, $\sigma^{-0.5}$, $\rho_v^{-0.5}$, $\rho_l^{0.81}$, $q^{-0.29}$, and $H^{0.69}$.

Insinger gave values of y and x for various liquids, for use with ft., lb., hr., °F., B.Th.U. units, as follows:

TABLE XII. *Constants for Use in Expression* (93).

	y	x
Water	$0.112H/\theta$	$0.0097H$
Isobutanol . . .	$1.18H/\theta$	$0.099H$
n-butanol . . .	$1.13H/\theta$	$0.095H$
Isopropanol . .	$1.00H/\theta$	$0.079H$
Carbon tetrachloride .	$3.85H/\theta$	$0.249H$
Toluene . . .	$2.56H/\theta$	$0.186H$

It will be noticed that neither viscosity nor size appears, which is consistent with the results of other observers.

For water, (93) reduces to:

$$\log(0.112H/\theta) = 0.363 + 0.923 \log(0.0097H) -$$
$$- 0.047(\log 0.0097H)^2. \qquad (94)$$

EXAMPLE

Find the rate of heat transfer to water boiling at 212° F. on a surface maintained at 242° F.

Solution. Temperature difference, θ, between surface and boiling water = (242−212) = 30 F.° Hence

$$\log 0 \cdot 112 + \log H - \log 30$$

$$= 0 \cdot 363 + 0 \cdot 923 \log 0 \cdot 0097 +$$

$$+ 0 \cdot 923 \log H - 0 \cdot 047 (\log H + \log 0 \cdot 0097)^2$$

$$= 0 \cdot 363 - (0 \cdot 923 \times 2 \cdot 013) +$$

$$+ 0 \cdot 923 \log H - 0 \cdot 047 (\log^2 H - 4 \cdot 02 \log H + 4 \cdot 05).$$

Whence

$$\log H (1 - 0 \cdot 923 - 0 \cdot 189) + 0 \cdot 047 \log^2 H$$

$$= 0 \cdot 951 + 1 \cdot 477 + 0 \cdot 363 - 1 \cdot 857 - 0 \cdot 190 = 0 \cdot 74$$

or

$$0 \cdot 047 \log^2 H - 0 \cdot 112 \log H = 0 \cdot 74,$$

which is satisfied by $H = 2 \cdot 3 \times 10^5$ B.Th.U./ft.^{2} hr., and H/θ, the heat transfer coefficient = $(2 \cdot 3 \times 10^5)/30 = 7,700$ B.Th.U./ft.^{2} hr. °F., which is in quite reasonable agreement with the corresponding values of about 8,000 and 9,000 B.Th.U./ft.^{2} hr. °F. given by Figs. 45 and 47.

Effect of pressure. The heat transfer coefficient, α, for a liquid boiling on a submerged surface, for any given temperature difference, θ, increases as the pressure and the consequent boiling-point are increased above atmospheric, and decreases as the pressure and the consequent boiling-point are decreased below atmospheric. For any given pressure, as already shown for atmospheric pressure, α at first increases with increasing θ, but at a certain point suddenly begins to decrease so that, with further increase of θ, the actual rate of heat transfer decreases. This is illustrated in Fig. 47, which is based mainly on the results of Braunlich [9] and Cryder and Finalborgo [10], and shows the heat transfer coefficients for temperature differences 10 to 100 F.°, for pressures corresponding to boiling-points of 210° F., 190° F., and 170° F. respectively.

Several workers have found that the increase of the heat transfer coefficient with pressure, for any given temperature difference, persists almost up to the critical point, but Cichelli and Bonilla [11] have shown recently that the temperature difference at the maximum rate of boiling heat transfer decreases with increase of pressure, so that the maximum rate of heat transfer, or maximum flux of heat, occurs at a pressure about one-third the critical. They correlated the results for water,

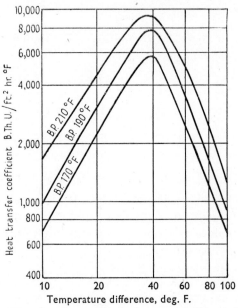

Fig. 47. Heat transfer coefficients for water boiling at 210° F., 190° F., and 170° F. on submerged surfaces.

ethanol, benzene, propane, n-pentane, n-heptane, and mixtures of water and butanol, water and ethanol, and water and acetone, by plotting the maximum rate of heat transfer per unit area, H_{max}, divided by the critical pressure, p_c, against the ratio of the actual to the critical pressure, p/p_c, and found that the results for all the liquids fell, with a certain amount of scatter, on a single curve. The results for dirty surfaces were about 15 per cent. above those for clean surfaces, probably because the vapour bubbles were freed more easily from them. Their curve is shown in Fig. 48, which gives also a curve for p/p_c between 0 and 0·1 on a magnified scale.

The apparently good correlation in Fig. 48 is, however, probably due to the fact that the organic liquids used had rather similar physical properties at their boiling-points, and it is therefore not advisable to apply the curve to water, which has very different properties. Cichelli and Bonilla's experiments did

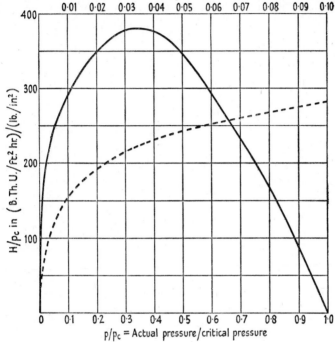

FIG. 48. Maximum heat flux for water boiling at different pressures on submerged surfaces. Upper scale corresponds to dotted curve.

include water, but only over a very limited range, since their heater was not powerful enough for the peak value to be reached even at the lower pressures. The critical pressure for water is $218\frac{1}{2}$ atmospheres, or 3,220 lb./in.², so p/p_c for water boiling at atmospheric pressure is 0·0046. At this point it will be seen from Fig. 48 that $H/p_c = 112$, whence $H = 112 \times 3220 = 360,000$ B.Th.U./ft.² hr., which is reasonably near the values found directly by other workers, and quoted on p. 177. At higher pressures the agreement is much less good. The peak density predicted at a pressure $\frac{1}{3}$ the critical is 1,400,000 B.Th.U./ft.² hr.

but McAdams [12] has measured values of 2,100,000 B.Th.U./ ft.^{2} hr. at 83 atmospheres, and the flux was still increasing with pressure.

In Fig. 49 the critical temperature difference between surface and boiling liquid at which the maximum boiling rate is given, as obtained from Cichelli and Bonilla's experiments on ethanol,

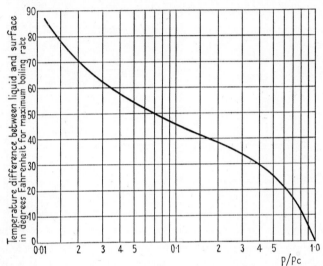

FIG. 49. Critical temperature difference corresponding to maximum boiling rate.

benzene, propane, etc., is plotted for ratios of p/p_c from 0·01 to 1·0.

Effect of scale deposit. Where the surface coefficients are so high, as for condensing steam and boiling liquids, the effects even of thin layers of dirt or scale can be very serious. Thus 1/100 in. of scale of conductivity 1 B.Th.U./ft.^{2} hr. °F. would be equivalent to a resistance of 1/1200, which is of the same order as that at the surfaces in many cases, and would thus cause an approximate reduction of 50 per cent. in the overall heat transfer. Taking into consideration also the dependence of both steam side and boiling side coefficients on surface conditions, it is easy to see that calculations based on work carried out under controlled laboratory conditions can give only a rough idea of the heat transfer to be expected in practice, and may suggest values much higher than those obtainable. The table below, based on experiments of Pridgeon and Badger [13], is an example: it gives the overall heat transfer coefficients, U, from steam condensing on the inside of a submerged horizontal tube to water boiling on the

TABLE XIII. *Overall Coefficients of Heat Transfer from Steam Condensing inside a Submerged Horizontal Tube to Water boiling Outside*

Overall θ in F.°	18	27	36	45	54
U, rusty iron	280	300	325	350	375
U, clean iron	300	385	460	535	610
U, slightly dirty copper	580	780	950	1,120	..
U, polished copper	820	1,110	1,470	1,810	2,120

outside. It will be seen that the overall heat transfer for the rusty iron is very approximately only $\frac{1}{4}$ to $\frac{1}{5}$ that for the polished copper.

BOILING INSIDE TUBES

In both forced circulation and natural circulation evaporators unevaporated liquid recirculates through the tubes, entering at the saturation temperature corresponding to the pressure in the vapour space. Boiling does not start right at the bottom of the tubes, owing to the slight increase in boiling-point caused by the hydrostatic head, but as the liquid flows up the tube, a point is reached at which actual boiling begins. Thus, if the tube is treated as a whole, the coefficients obtained are not true boiling coefficients, since a part of the tube in which the liquid is not boiling is included.

Forced circulation vertical tube evaporators. For forced circulation vertical tube evaporators, Boarts *et alia* [14] found that for runs in which Re exceeded 65,000, corresponding to inlet velocities above $3\frac{1}{2}$ ft./sec., the boiling side coefficients for the whole tube were about 25 per cent. above those which would be given by expression (53) for forced convection in flow through tubes, i.e. $Nu = 0.023Re^{0.8}Pr^{0.4}$. For lower feed rates, in which a higher proportion of the water was evaporated per pass, they averaged about 140 per cent. above those given by

(53). Kirschbaum [15] found similarly that for a vertical tube evaporator the excess of the coefficients over those indicated by (53) increased as the feed rate was reduced, and also as the temperature difference was increased. For a velocity of 10 ft./sec. the excess was 26 and 84 per cent. at temperature differences of 9 and 27 F.° respectively; for 3 ft./sec. 26 and 105 per cent. respectively.

For water boiling at atmospheric pressure the coefficients calculated from (53) for a 1-in. tube and velocities of 5, 10, 15, 20 ft./sec. work out at about 1,700, 3,000, 4,100, 5,000 B.Th.U./ft.² hr. °F. respectively, so that in forced circulation evaporators they should be well above this. Hence if steam were used for heating, the major resistance would be on the steam side unless the condensation were dropwise. Taking a steam side coefficient of 1,000 B.Th.U./ft.² hr. °F., the overall coefficients would become about 600, 750, 800, and 820 respectively, not allowing for any resistance in the tube wall. In practice, as will be seen later, lower coefficients are usually found.

Natural circulation evaporators. The boiling side heat transfer coefficients are usually considerably less for natural than for forced circulation evaporators, because of the much lower feed velocities. Also, in this case, as for submerged surfaces, they increase with increased temperature difference or with increased boiling-point. Surface tension also has a very marked effect. Thus, Stroebe *et alia* [16], working with a long tube vertical natural circulation evaporator, found that, by decreasing the surface tension of water 50 per cent. by the addition of 'Duponol', the heat transfer coefficients on the boiling side were increased by 100 to 300 per cent. On the other hand, increase of viscosity decreases the coefficients. Thus, Coates and Badger [17], using steam as the heating agent for boiling molasses solutions, found that practically all the resistance was on the boiling side.

Overall heat transfer coefficients for natural circulation evaporators. Badger and Shephard [18] found the overall coefficients given below for a basket-type evaporator with vertical tubes 2 in. diameter and 2 ft. length, in which water was boiled by condensing steam on their outer surfaces.

TABLE XIV. *Overall Coefficients of Heat Transfer from Steam condensing outside Vertical Tubes to Water boiling inside*

Overall θ in F.°	10	20	30	40	50	60
Overall α for B.P. 140° F.	120	205	270	320	350	370
Overall α for B.P. 167° F.	220	320	400	440	480	500
Overall α for B.P. 212° F.	320	440	500	520	..	..

Foust *et alia* [19], boiling water at 154° F. by condensing steam on short tubes (2½ in. diameter, 4 ft. length), found corresponding values of 80 to 340 B.Th.U./ft.² hr. °F. The coefficients increased as the level of the liquid was lowered, and as the temperature difference or the boiling-point was increased.

BIBLIOGRAPHY

HEAT TRANSFER TO BOILING LIQUIDS

1. JAKOB, M. 'Heat Transfer in Evaporation and Condensation.' *Mech. Eng.* 1936, **58**, 643.
2. (KAISER.) See FRITZ, W. *Wärmeübergang an siedende Flüssigkeiten.* V.D.I. Verfahr. 1937 No. 5.
3. NUKIYAMA, S. 'Heat transmitted from Metal to Boiling Water under Atmospheric Pressure.' *J. Soc. Mech. Eng. Japan,* 1934, **37**, 367, 553.
4. ABBOTT, M. D., and COMLEY, W. D. Mass. Inst. Tech. Thesis, 1938.
5. SAUER, E. T., and COOPER, H. B. H. 'Heat Transfer to Boiling Liquids.' *Mech. Eng.* 1938, **60**, 669.
6. RHODES, F. H., and BRIDGES, C. H. 'Heat Transfer to Boiling Liquids.' *Ind. Eng. Chem.* 1938, **30**, 1401, or *Trans. Am. Inst. Chem. Eng.* 1939, **35**, 73.
7. INSINGER, T. H., and BLISS, H. 'Transmission of Heat to Boiling Liquids.' Ibid. 1940, **36**, 491.
8. JAKOB, M. 'The Influence of Pressure on Heat Transfer in Evaporation.' *Proc. 5th International Congress Applied Mechanics,* 1938, 561.
9. BRAUNLICH, R. H. Mass. Inst. Tech. Thesis, 1941.
10. CRYDER, D. S., and FINALBORGO, A. C. 'Heat Transmission from Metal Surfaces to Boiling Liquids.' *Trans. Am. Inst. Chem. Eng.* 1937, **33**, 346.
11. CICHELLI, M. T., and BONILLA, C. F. 'Heat Transfer to Liquids Boiling under Pressure.' Ibid. 1945, **41**, 755.
12. McADAMS, W. H. 'High Densities of Heat Flux from Metal to Water.' *N.E.P.A. Heat Transfer Symposium,* Tennessee, 1947, vol. i, 17.

13. PRIDGEON, L. A., and BADGER, W. L. 'Studies in Evaporator Design.' *Ind. Eng. Chem.* 1924, **16**, 469.
14. BOARTS, R. M., BADGER, W. L., and MEISENBURG, S. J. 'Temperature Drops and Liquid-film Heat Transfer Coefficients in Vertical Tubes.' *Trans. Am. Inst. Chem. Eng.* 1937, **33**, 363.
15. KIRSCHBAUM, E. 'Wärmeübergang am senkrechten Verdampferrohr.' *Forsch. Gebiete Ingenieurwes.*, Heft No. 375, 1935.
16. STROEBE, G., BAKER, E. M., and BADGER, W. L. 'Boiling Film Heat Transfer Coefficients in a long Tube Vertical Evaporator.' *Trans. Am. Inst. Chem. Eng.* 1939, **35**, 17.
17. COATES, J., and BADGER, W. L. 'The Effects of Viscosity on Coefficients of Heat Transfer in Forced Circulation Evaporators.' Ibid. 1936, **32**, 49.
18. BADGER, S. L., and SHEPHARD, P. W. Part I, 'Studies in Evaporator Design'. Ibid. 1920, **13**, 139.
19. FOUST, A. S., BAKER, E. M., and BADGER, W. L. 'Liquid Velocity and Coefficients of Heat Transfer in a Natural Circulation Evaporator.' *Ind. Eng. Chem.* 1939, **31**, 206.

TABLES

TABLE XV. *Values of $f(t) = 1{\cdot}73 \times 10^{-9}(t+460)^4$ for t from 10° F. to 3,000° F.*

t	f(t)	t	f(t)	t	f(t)	t	f(t)	t	f(t)
10	84	430	1,090	850	5,090	1,270	15,400	1,690	37,000
20	92	440	1,140	860	5,250	1,280	15,800	1,700	37,700
30	100	450	1,190	870	5,410	1,290	16,200	1,710	38,400
40	108	460	1,240	880	5,580	1,300	16,600	1,720	39,100
50	117	470	1,290	890	5,750	1,310	17,000	1,730	39,800
60	126	480	1,350	900	5,920	1,320	17,400	1,740	40,500
70	136	490	1,410	910	6,100	1,330	17,800	1,750	41,200
80	147	500	1,470	920	6,270	1,340	18,200	1,760	42,000
90	158	510	1,530	930	6,450	1,350	18,600	1,770	42,800
100	170	520	1,590	940	6,650	1,360	19,000	1,780	43,600
110	183	530	1,660	950	6,850	1,370	19,400	1,790	44,400
120	196	540	1,730	960	7,050	1,380	19,800	1,800	45,200
130	210	550	1,800	970	7,250	1,390	20,300	1,810	45,900
140	224	560	1,870	980	7,450	1,400	20,700	1,820	46,700
150	240	570	1,940	990	7,650	1,410	21,200	1,830	47,600
160	256	580	2,020	1,000	7,860	1,420	21,600	1,840	48,400
170	273	590	2,100	1,010	8,080	1,430	22,100	1,850	49,300
180	290	600	2,180	1,020	8,300	1,440	22,600	1,860	50,100
190	309	610	2,260	1,030	8,520	1,450	23,100	1,870	51,000
200	328	620	2,350	1,040	8,760	1,460	23,600	1,880	51,900
210	349	630	2,440	1,050	9,000	1,470	24,100	1,890	52,800
220	370	640	2,530	1,060	9,240	1,480	24,600	1,900	53,600
230	392	650	2,630	1,070	9,480	1,490	25,100	1,910	54,500
240	415	660	2,730	1,080	9,730	1,500	25,600	1,920	55,400
250	440	670	2,830	1,090	9,990	1,510	26,100	1,930	56,400
260	465	680	2,930	1,100	10,200	1,520	26,600	1,940	57,300
270	491	690	3,030	1,110	10,500	1,530	27,100	1,950	58,300
280	519	700	3,130	1,120	10,800	1,540	27,600	1,960	59,300
290	548	710	3,240	1,130	11,000	1,550	28,200	1,970	60,300
300	577	720	3,350	1,140	11,300	1,560	28,700	1,980	61,300
310	607	730	3,460	1,150	11,600	1,570	29,300	1,990	62,300
320	639	740	3,580	1,160	11,900	1,580	29,900	2,000	63,300
330	674	750	3,710	1,170	12,200	1,590	30,500	2,100	74,300
340	710	760	3,830	1,180	12,500	1,600	31,100	2,200	86,600
350	746	770	3,960	1,190	12,800	1,610	31,800	2,300	100,000
360	782	780	4,090	1,200	13,100	1,620	32,400	2,400	116,000
370	821	790	4,220	1,210	13,400	1,630	33,000	2,500	133,000
380	861	800	4,360	1,220	13,700	1,640	33,600	2,600	152,000
390	903	810	4,500	1,230	14,000	1,650	34,200	2,700	173,000
400	946	820	4,640	1,240	14,400	1,660	34,900	2,800	195,000
410	990	830	4,780	1,250	14,800	1,670	35,600	2,900	221,000
420	1,040	840	4,930	1,260	15,100	1,680	36,300	3,000	248,000
430	1,090	850	5,090	1,270	15,400	1,690	37,000		

TABLE XVI. *Emissivities of Various Surfaces*

	0° F.–100° F. (11·3μ–9·3μ)	250° F. (7·3μ)	500° F. (5·4μ)	1,000° F. (3·6μ)	2,000° F. (2·1μ)	3,000° F. (1·5μ)
Pure polished metals (provided not of exceptionally high electrical resistivity)	0·04	0·05	0·06	0·07	0·14	0·25
White surfaces, white or cream paints or bricks, etc.	0·95	0·94	0·88	0·70	0·45	0·35
Lampblack, acetylene soot, camphor soot, Pt black, black velvet, etc. . .	0·97	0·97	0·97	0·97	0·97	0·97
Dark painted surfaces, dark bricks, etc. . . .	0·95	0·94	0·90	0·85	0·80	0·75
Various Al paints . .	0·40–0·70	..	..	..	..	..
Various lacs and oils . .	0·50–0·90	..	..	..	..	..
Linseed oil on Al foil:						
Low thickness . .	..	0·09	..	..	..	..
One coat oil . . .	..	0·56	..	..	..	..
Two coats oil . .	..	0·57	..	..	..	..
About a hundred different refractories, ceramics, bricks, tiles . . .	0·9	0·9	0·65–0·85	0·3–0·8	0·3–0·9	0·2–0·9
Iron and steel						
Pure polished . . .	0·06	0·06	0·08	0·12	0·22	0·26
Polished steel casting . .	..	..	..	0·49	0·56	..
,, ,, ,, . .	0·07	0·08	0·10	0·14	0·23	0·28
Rolled sheet steel . .	0·56	..	..	..	..	..
Ground sheet steel . .	..	..	..	0·41	0·61	..
Smooth sheet iron . .	..	..	..	0·48	0·60	..
Bright cast iron . .	0·16	0·22	0·30	..	..	..
Freshly drawn cast iron .	0·44	..	..	..	..	..
Cast plate iron: smooth .	0·80	..	..	..	..	..
,, ,, ,, rough .	0·82	..	..	..	..	..
Cast iron with skin . .	0·81	..	..	..	..	..
,, ,, ,, ,, . .	..	0·60	..	..	..	..
,, ,, ,, ,, . .	0·66	..	..	..	..	..
Cast iron lathe turned .	..	..	..	..	0·70	..
Rough ingot steel . .	..	..	..	..	0·95	..
Ground sheet steel . .	..	..	..	..	0·61	..
Rough steel plate . .	0·94	0·95	0·97	0·98	..	..
Rolled sheet steel . .	0·66	..	..	..	..	..
Cast iron: oxidized . .	0·57	0·61	0·66	0·75	..	..
,, ,, ,, . .	0·63	0·63	0·63	0·52	..	..
Oxidized iron . . .	..	0·74	..	..	..	..
Smoothly oxidized electrolytic iron . . .	0·78	0·78	0·80	0·83	..	..
Matt wrought iron, oxidized	0·95	0·95	0·95	..	..	..
Rough cast iron, oxidized .	0·98	..	..	..	..	..
Iron with rough oxide layer	0·81	..	..	..	..	..
Corroded sheet iron . .	..	0·74	..	..	..	..
Sheet steel with rough oxide	0·80	..	..	..	..	..
Sheet steel with shining oxide	0·82	..	..	..	..	..
Oxidized steel, after long heating	0·84	0·88	0·93	0·96	..	..
Oxidized steel . . .	0·79	0·79	0·79	0·79	..	..
Calorized steel . . .	0·50	0·51	0·53	0·56	..	..
Iron oxide	..	..	..	0·85	0·89	..
,, ,, . . .	..	..	..	0·85	0·88	..
Black iron oxide . .	..	0·56	..	..	..	..
Red iron oxide . . .	0·96	..	..	..	..	..
Molten cast iron . .	..	..	..	..	0·29 (at 2,400° F.)	..

TABLE XVI (*cont.*)

	0° F.–100° F. (*11·3μ–9·3μ*)	250° F. (*7·3μ*)	500° F. (*5·4μ*)	1,000° F. (*3·6μ*)	2,000° F. (*2·1μ*)	3,000° F. (*1·5μ*)
Molten mild steel . .	..	..	..	..	..	0·28
Oil on polished iron:						
Very thin . . .	0·06	..	..	..	..	..
0·0008 in. thick . .	0·22	..	..	..	..	..
0·002 in. thick . .	0·45	..	..	..	..	..
0·004 in. thick . .	0·65	..	..	..	..	..
0·008 in. thick . .	0·81	..	..	..	..	..
Very thick . . .	0·83	..	..	..	..	..

See also McAdams, *Heat Transmission*, pp. 393–6.

TABLE XVII. *Heat Loss H, by Radiation and Convection to Surroundings at 65° F. from Unit Area of a Large Body, of Temperature t and Emissivity E*

$$H = 0·3(t-65)^{5/4} + 1·73\times10^{-9}E\{(t+460)^4 - (65+460)^4\} \text{ B.Th.U./ft.}^2\text{hr.} \quad \text{when} \quad t > 65° \text{F.}$$

$$H = -0·3(65-t)^{5/4} + 1·73\times10^{-9}E\{(t+460)^4 - (65+460)^4\} \text{ B.Th.U./ft.}^2\text{hr.} \quad \text{when} \quad t < 65° \text{F.}$$

$$\alpha = H/(t-65) \text{ B.Th.U./ft.}^2\text{hr. }°\text{F.}$$

$t°$ F.	$E=1$		$E=0.9$		$E=0.7$		$E=0.5$		$E=0.3$		$E=0.1$	
	H	α	H	α	H	α	H	α	H	α	H	α
0	−109	1·68	−104	1·60	−93	1·43	−82	1·27	−72	1·10	−61	0·94
10	−92	1·67	−87	1·58	−78	1·41	−68	1·24	−59	1·07	−50	0·90
20	−74	1·65	−70	1·56	−62	1·39	−54	1·21	−46·6	1·04	−38·7	0·86
30	−57	1·63	−54	1·54	−47·7	1·36	−41·4	1·18	−35·0	1·00	−28·7	0·82
40	−40·1	1·60	−37·8	1·51	−33·1	1·32	−28·4	1·14	−23·8	0·95	−19·1	0·76
50	−23·2	1·55	−21·8	1·45	−18·9	1·26	−16·0	1·07	−13·2	0·88	−10·3	0·69
60	−7·2	1·44	−6·7	1·34	−5·7	1·14	−4·7	0·94	−3·7	0·74	−2·7	0·55
64	−1·30	1·30	−1·20	1·20	−1·00	1·00	−0·80	0·80	−0·60	0·60	−0·40	0·40
66	1·30	1·30	1·20	1·20	1·00	1·00	0·80	0·80	0·60	0·60	0·40	0·40
70	7·3	1·47	6·8	1·37	5·8	1·16	4·8	0·96	3·8	0·76	2·8	0·55
80	24·6	1·64	23·0	1·53	19·8	1·32	16·7	1·11	13·6	0·90	10·4	0·69
90	43·7	1·75	41·0	1·64	35·6	1·42	30·2	1·21	24·8	0·99	19·5	0·78
100	64	1·83	60	1·72	53	1·50	44·9	1·28	37·1	1·06	29·4	0·84
110	86	1·91	81	1·80	71	1·57	60	1·35	50	1·12	39·9	0·89
120	109	1·99	103	1·87	90	1·64	77	1·40	64	1·17	51	0·93
130	134	2·06	126	1·94	110	1·70	95	1·45	79	1·21	63	0·97
140	159	2·12	150	2·00	131	1·75	113	1·50	94	1·25	76	1·01
150	186	2·18	175	2·05	153	1·80	132	1·55	110	1·29	89	1·04
160	213	2·24	201	2·11	176	1·85	151	1·59	126	1·33	102	1·07
170	242	2·30	228	2·17	200	1·90	171	1·63	143	1·36	115	1·10
180	272	2·36	256	2·22	225	1·95	192	1·67	161	1·40	129	1·12

TABLE XVII (cont.)

i° F.	E = 0.1		E = 0.3		E = 0.5		E = 0.7		E = 0.9		E = 1	
	H	α	H	α	H	α	H	α	H	α	H	α
190	143	1·15	179	1·43	214	1·71	250	2·00	285	2·28	303	2·42
200	158	1·17	197	1·46	237	1·75	276	2·04	315	2·33	335	2·48
300	321	1·36	410	1·74	499	2·12	588	2·50	677	2·88	722	3·07
400	510	1·53	673	2·01	836	2·50	999	2·98	1,160	3·47	1,240	3·71
500	731	1·68	998	2·30	1,270	2·91	1,530	3·52	1,800	4·14	1,930	4·45
600	976	1·82	1,390	2·59	1,800	3·36	2,210	4·13	2,620	4·90	2,820	5·28
700	1,260	1·98	1,860	2·92	2,460	3·86	3,060	4·81	3,660	5·76	3,960	6·23
800	1,570	2·14	2,420	3·29	3,260	4·44	4,110	5·59	4,960	6·75	5,380	7·32
900	1,930	2·31	3,090	3·70	4,240	5·08	5,400	6·47	6,550	7·85	7,130	8·54
1,000	2,320	2·49	3,870	4·14	5,420	5·79	6,960	7·45	8,510	9·10	9,280	9·93
1,100	2,770	2·68	4,800	4·63	6,820	6·59	8,840	8·54	10,900	10·5	11,900	11·5
1,200	3,280	2·89	5,880	5·18	8,480	7·47	11,100	9·76	13,700	12·1	15,000	13·2
1,300	3,840	3·11	7,140	5·78	10,400	8·45	13,700	11·1	17,000	13·8	18,700	15·1
1,400	4,480	3·36	8,600	6·44	12,700	9·52	16,800	12·6	20,900	15·7	23,000	17·2
1,500	5,190	3·62	10,300	7·16	15,400	10·7	20,400	14·2	25,500	17·8	28,100	19·6
1,600	5,980	3·90	12,200	7·95	18,400	12·0	24,600	16·0	30,800	20·1	33,900	22·1
1,700	6,870	4·20	14,400	8·80	21,900	13·4	29,400	18·0	36,900	22·6	40,600	24·9
1,800	7,860	4·53	16,900	9·72	25,900	14·9	34,900	20·1	43,900	25·3	48,400	27·9
1,900	8,960	4·88	19,700	10·7	30,400	16·5	41,100	22·4	51,800	28·2	57,100	31·1
2,000	10,200	5·26	22,800	11·8	35,500	18·3	48,100	24·9	60,800	31·4	67,100	34·7

TABLE XVIII. *Physical Properties of Air, Carbon dioxide, Hydrogen, Water vapour, and Water*

AIR

(applicable also with very little error to carbon monoxide, nitrogen, and oxygen)

Temp. °F.	k B.Th.U. ft.hr.°F.	μ lb. ft. hr.	ν ft.² hr.	c B.Th.U. lb. °F.	s B.Th.U. ft.³ °F.	ρ lb. ft.³	Prandtl Number $\dfrac{s\nu}{k}\left(=\dfrac{\mu c}{k}\right)$ Dimensionless	$\dfrac{gs}{k\nu}\left(=\dfrac{gc\rho^2}{k\mu}\right)$ $\dfrac{10^7}{ft.^3}$
−100	0·0109	0·0328	0·300	0·238	0·0262	0·110	0·73	331
0	0·0133	0·0400	0·467	0·239	0·0205	0·086	0·72	137
32	0·0140	0·0420	0·52	0·240	0·0194	0·081	0·72	110
100	0·0154	0·0462	0·65	0·240	0·0170	0·071	0·72	70
200	0·0174	0·0520	0·86	0·241	0·0144	0·060	0·72	39·8
300	0·0193	0·058	1·10	0·243	0·0126	0·052	0·72	24·5
400	0·0212	0·063	1·36	0·245	0·0113	0·0460	0·72	16·2
500	0·0231	0·068	1·64	0·247	0·0102	0·0412	0·72	11·2
600	0·0250	0·072	1·94	0·250	0·0093	0·0373	0·72	8·0
700	0·0268	0·077	2·25	0·253	0·0086	0·0341	0·72	5·9
800	0·0286	0·081	2·58	0·256	0·0080	0·0314	0·72	4·48
900	0·0303	0·085	2·93	0·259	0·0075	0·0291	0·72	3·50
1,000	0·0319	0·089	3·30	0·262	0·0071	0·0271	0·73	2·80
1,100	0·0336	0·093	3·68	0·265	0·0067	0·0253	0·73	2·25
1,200	0·0353	0·097	4·07	0·268	0·0064	0·0238	0·74	1·85
1,300	0·0369	0·101	4·47	0·271	0·0061	0·0225	0·74	1·53
1,400	0·0385	0·104	4·88	0·274	0·0058	0·0213	0·74	1·28
1,500	0·0400	0·108	5·3	0·276	0·0056	0·0202	0·74	1·10
1,600	0·0415	0·111	5·8	0·278	0·0053	0·0192	0·74	0·91
1,700	0·0430	0·115	6·3	0·280	0·0051	0·0183	0·75	0·78
1,800	0·0444	0·118	6·7	0·282	0·00495	0·0175	0·75	0·68
1,900	0·0458	0·121	7·2	0·284	0·00477	0·0168	0·75	0·60
2,000	0·0471	0·124	7·7	0·286	0·00460	0·0161	0·75	0·53
2,100	0·0484	0·127	8·2	0·287	0·00444	0·0155	0·75	0·465
2,200	0·0496	0·129	8·7	0·288	0·00429	0·0149	0·75	0·415
2,300	0·051	0·131	9·2	0·290	0·00415	0·0143	0·75	0·375
2,400	0·051	0·132	9·6	0·291	0·00402	0·0138	0·76	0·340
2,500	0·051	0·133	10·1	0·292	0·00390	0·0133	0·76	0·310
2,600	0·052	0·135	10·5	0·293	0·00378	0·0129	0·76	0·286
2,700	0·052	0·136	10·9	0·294	0·00367	0·0125	0·76	0·267
2,800	0·053	0·137	11·3	0·295	0·00357	0·0121	0·76	0·248
2,900	0·053	0·138	11·8	0·296	0·00348	0·0117	0·77	0·230
3,000	0·054	0·139	12·2	0·297	0·00339	0·0114	0·76	0·213

TABLE XVIII (*cont.*)

CARBON DIOXIDE

Temp. °F.	k $\dfrac{B.Th.U.}{ft.hr.°F.}$	μ $\dfrac{lb.}{ft.hr.}$	ν $\dfrac{ft.^2}{hr.}$	c $\dfrac{B.Th.U.}{lb.°F.}$	s $\dfrac{B.Th.U.}{ft.^3 °F.}$	ρ $\dfrac{lb.}{ft.^3}$	Prandtl Number $\dfrac{s\nu}{k}\left(=\dfrac{\mu c}{k}\right)$ Dimensionless	$\dfrac{gs}{k\nu}\left(=\dfrac{gc\rho^2}{k\mu}\right)$ $\dfrac{10^7}{ft.^3}$
0	0·0076	0·0317	0·241	0·184	0·0246	0·132	0·76	556
32	0·0084	0·0339	0·276	0·194	0·0238	0·124	0·78	427
100	0·0101	0·0379	0·352	0·203	0·0220	0·108	0·76	257
200	0·0125	0·0439	0·480	0·216	0·0199	0·092	0·76	138
300	0·0150	0·0497	0·63	0·227	0·0182	0·080	0·75	80
400	0·0174	0·055	0·79	0·237	0·0167	0·070	0·75	50
500	0·0198	0·060	0·96	0·247	0·0156	0·063	0·75	34·5
600	0·0222	0·065	1·15	0·256	0·0146	0·057	0·75	23·8
700	0·0246	0·070	1·35	0·263	0·0137	0·052	0·75	17·1
800	0·0270	0·075	1·56	0·269	0·0129	0·0480	0·75	12·6
900	0·0294	0·079	1·78	0·275	0·0122	0·0445	0·74	9·7
1,000	0·0317	0·083	2·01	0·280	0·0116	0·0414	0·73	7·5
1,100	0·0339	0·087	2·25	0·284	0·0110	0·0387	0·73	5·9
1,200	0·0360	0·091	2·50	0·288	0·0105	0·0364	0·73	4·83
1,300	0·0380	0·095	2·76	0·292	0·0100	0·0344	0·73	3·90
1,400	0·0399	0·099	3·04	0·295	0·0096	0·0325	0·73	3·28
1,500	0·0418	0·103	3·33	0·298	0·0092	0·0308	0·73	2·73
1,600	0·0436	0·107	3·63	0·301	0·0088	0·0293	0·74	2·31
1,700	0·0453	0·110	3·93	0·303	0·0085	0·0280	0·73	1·97
1,800	9·0469	0·113	4·22	0·305	0·0082	0·0268	0·73	1·71
1,900	0·0484	0·116	4·52	0·307	0·0079	0·0257	0·73	1·50
2,000	0·050	0·119	4·83	0·309	0·0076	0·0247	0·74	1·32
2,100	0·051	0·122	5·15	0·311	0·0074	0·0237	0·74	1·16
2,200	0·052	0·125	5·5	0·313	0·0071	0·0228	0·74	1·03
2,300	0·054	0·128	5·8	0·314	0·0069	0·0219	0·74	0·91
2,400	0·056	0·130	6·2	0·316	0·0067	0·0211	0·74	0·80
2,500	0·057	0·132	6·5	0·317	0·0065	0·0204	0·74	0·72
2,600	0·058	0·134	6·8	0·318	0·0063	0·0197	0·74	0·66
2,700	0·059	0·136	7·1	0·319	0·0061	0·0191	0·74	0·60
2,800	0·060	0·138	7·4	0·320	0·0059	0·0185	0·74	0·55
2,900	0·061	0·140	7·7	0·321	0·0058	0·0180	0·74	0·51
3,000	0·061	0·141	8·1	0·322	0·0056	0·0175	0·74	0·47

TABLE XVIII (cont.)

HYDROGEN

Temp. °F.	k B.Th.U. / ft.hr.°F.	μ lb. / ft.hr.	ν ft.² / hr.	c B.Th.U. / lb.°F.	s B.Th.U. / ft.³ °F.	ρ lb. / ft.³	Prandtl Number $\dfrac{s\nu}{k}\left(=\dfrac{\mu c}{k}\right)$ Dimensionless	$\dfrac{gs}{k\nu}\left(=\dfrac{gc\rho^2}{k\mu}\right)$ 10^5 / ft.³
−100	0·079	0·0164	2·14	3·37	0·0258	0·0077	0·70	632
0	0·094	0·0194	3·22	3·39	0·0204	0·0060	0·70	280
32	0·099	0·0203	3·62	3·40	0·0191	0·0056	0·70	221
100	0·109	0·0223	4·53	3·42	0·0168	0·00491	0·70	141
200	0·122	0·0249	6·0	3·44	0·0143	0·00416	0·70	81
300	0·135	0·0273	7·6	3·45	0·0125	0·00361	0·70	50
400	0·146	0·0297	9·3	3·46	0·0111	0·00319	0·70	34
500	0·157	0·0319	11·2	3·47	0·0099	0·00286	0·70	23·3
600	0·168	0·0341	13·2	3·48	0·0090	0·00259	0·70	16·8
700	0·178	0·0361	15·2	3·49	0·0083	0·00237	0·71	12·7
800	0·188	0·0380	17·4	3·49	0·0076	0·00218	0·71	9·6
900	0·198	0·0399	19·8	3·50	0·0071	0·00202	0·71	7·5
1,000	0·208	0·0419	22·3	3·51	0·0066	0·00188	0·71	5·9
1,100	0·219	0·0438	24·9	3·53	0·0062	0·00176	0·71	4·7
1,200	0·229	0·0458	27·7	3·55	0·0059	0·00165	0·71	3·8
1,300	0·240	0·0477	30·5	3·57	0·0056	0·00156	0·71	3·2
1,400	0·250	0·0496	33·5	3·59	0·0053	0·00148	0·72	2·6
1,500	0·260	0·051	36·7	3·62	0·0051	0·00140	0·72	2·21
1,600	0·270	0·053	39·9	3·64	0·00485	0·00133	0·72	1·87
1,700	0·280	0·055	43·1	3·67	0·00467	0·00127	0·72	1·60
1,800	0·289	0·056	46·1	3·70	0·00451	0·00122	0·72	1·40
1,900	0·298	0·058	49·2	3·73	0·00435	0·00117	0·72	1·23
2,000	0·307	0·059	52·0	3·76	0·00420	0·00112	0·72	1·09
2,100	0·315	0·060	56	3·78	0·00405	0·00107	0·72	0·96
2,200	0·323	0·061	59	3·81	0·00392	0·00103	0·72	0·85
2,300	0·331	0·062	62	3·83	0·00381	0·00100	0·72	0·76
2,400	0·338	0·063	66	3·86	0·00371	0·00096	0·72	0·69
2,500	0·345	0·064	69	3·88	0·00361	0·00093	0·72	0·63
2,600	0·352	0·065	72	3·91	0·00351	0·00090	0·72	0·57
2,700	0·359	0·066	76	3·94	0·00342	0·00087	0·73	0·52
2,800	0·366	0·067	80	3·97	0·00334	0·00084	0·73	0·47
2,900	0·373	0·068	84	4·00	0·00326	0·00082	0·73	0·43
3,000	0·380	0·069	87	4·02	0·00318	0·00079	0·73	0·40

TABLE XVIII (*cont.*)

WATER VAPOUR (ATMOSPHERIC PRESSURE)

Temp. °F.	k B.Th.U. ft.hr.°F.	μ lb. ft. hr.	ν ft.² hr.	c B.Th.U. lb. °F.	s B.Th.U. ft.³ °F.	ρ lb. ft.³	Prandtl Number $\frac{s\nu}{k}\left(=\frac{\mu c}{k}\right)$ Dimensionless	$\frac{gs}{k\nu}\left(=\frac{gc\rho^2}{k\mu}\right)$ $\frac{10^6}{ft.³}$
212	0·0145	0·0313	0·84	0·451	0·0168	0·0372	0·96	576
300	0·0171	0·0359	1·09	0·456	0·0149	0·0328	0·95	331
400	0·0200	0·0408	1·42	0·462	0·0133	0·0288	0·94	194
500	0·0228	0·0455	1·76	0·470	0·0121	0·0258	0·94	117
600	0·0257	0·051	2·19	0·477	0·0111	0·0233	0·94	82
700	0·0288	0·056	2·61	0·485	0·0103	0·0213	0·93	57
800	0·0321	0·061	3·08	0·494	0·0097	0·0196	0·92	40·6
900	0·0355	0·065	3·55	0·50	0·0092	0·0181	0·91	30·1
1,000	0·0388	0·069	4·08	0·51	0·0087	0·0169	0·91	22·6
1,100	0·0422	0·073	4·61	0·52	0·0082	0·0158	0·90	17·5
1,200	0·0457	0·077	5·2	0·53	0·0079	0·0149	0·88	13·9
1,300	0·0494	0·081	5·7	0·54	0·0075	0·0141	0·88	11·0
1,400	0·053	0·085	6·4	0·55	0·0073	0·0133	0·87	8·9
1,500	0·057	0·089	7·1	0·56	0·0070	0·0126	0·87	7·2
1,600	0·061	0·093	7·7	0·56	0·0068	0·0120	0·87	6·0
1,700	0·064	0·097	8·5	0·57	0·0066	0·0114	0·87	5·0
1,800	0·068	0·101	9·3	0·58	0·0064	0·0109	0·87	4·17
1,900	0·072	0·105	10·1	0·59	0·0062	0·0104	0·87	3·53
2,000	0·076	0·109	10·9	0·60	0·0060	0·0100	0·87	3·01
2,100	0·080	0·113	11·8	0·61	0·0058	0·0096	0·86	2·56
2,200	0·084	0·117	12·7	0·62	0·0057	0·0092	0·86	2·19
2,300	0·088	0·121	13·6	0·62	0·0055	0·0089	0·86	1·91
2,400	0·092	0·125	14·5	0·63	0·0054	0·0086	0·86	1·67
2,500	0·096	0·129	15·5	0·64	0·0053	0·0083	0·86	1·47
2,600	0·100	0·132	16·5	0·64	0·0051	0·0080	0·86	1·30
2,700	0·104	0·135	17·5	0·65	0·0050	0·0077	0·86	1·14
2,800	0·108	0·138	18·5	0·65	0·0049	0·0075	0·86	1·01
2,900	0·111	0·141	19·6	0·66	0·0048	0·0073	0·86	0·92
3,000	0·114	0·144	20·7	0·67	0·0047	0·0071	0·86	0·83

TABLE XVIII (*cont.*)

WATER

Temp. °F.	k B.Th.U. / ft.hr.°F.	μ lb. / ft. hr.	ν ft.² / hr.	c B.Th.U. / lb. °F.	s B.Th.U. / ft.³ °F.	ρ lb. / ft.³	Prandtl Number $\frac{s\nu}{k}\left(=\frac{\mu c}{k}\right)$ Dimensionless	$\frac{gs}{k\nu}\left(=\frac{gc\rho^2}{k\mu}\right)$ $\frac{10^{12}}{ft.^3}$
30	0·33	4·50	0·072	1·01	63	62	13·8	1·10
40	0·33	3·70	0·059	1·01	63	62	11·1	1·32
50	0·34	3·15	0·050	1·00	63	62	9·2	1·52
60	0·34	2·74	0·0439	1·00	62	62	7·95	1·71
70	0·35	2·39	0·0385	1·00	62	62	6·88	1·92
80	0·35	2·10	0·0337	1·00	62	62	5·93	2·16
90	0·36	1·85	0·0298	1·00	62	62	5·14	2·41
100	0·36	1·64	0·0265	1·00	62	62	4·53	2·67
110	0·37	1·47	0·0238	1·00	62	62	4·02	2·93
120	0·37	1·33	0·0216	1·00	62	62	3·61	3·20
130	0·37	1·23	0·0200	1·00	61	61	3·30	3·43
140	0·37	1·14	0·0186	1·00	61	61	3·05	3·66
150	0·38	1·05	0·0172	1·00	61	61	2·79	3·92
160	0·38	0·97	0·0159	1·00	61	61	2·56	4·18
170	0·38	0·89	0·0147	1·00	61	61	2·35	4·48
180	0·38	0·83	0·0137	1·00	61	61	2·17	4·78
190	0·39	0·78	0·0129	1·00	61	60	2·03	5·0
200	0·39	0·73	0·0121	1·00	60	60	1·88	5·3
210	0·39	0·68	0·0113	1·01	60	60	1·74	5·6
220	0·39	0·64	0·0107	1·01	60	60	1·63	5·8
230	0·40	0·61	0·0103	1·01	60	59	1·56	6·1
240	0·40	0·58	0·0098	1·015	60	59	1·47	6·4
250	0·40	0·55	0·0093	1·02	60	59	1·30	6·7
300	0·39	0·44	0·0077	1·025	59	57	1·13	8·0
350	0·39	0·36	0·0065	1·03	57	55	0·95	9·3
400	0·38	0·32	0·0060	1·04	56	53	0·87	10·1
450	0·37	0·29	0·0057	1·05	54	51	0·83	10·6
500	0·35	0·27	0·0056	1·06	51	49	0·82	10·9

CONVERSION FACTORS

Length, l
  1 cm. = $3 \cdot 28 \times 10^{-2}$ ft.   1 ft. = $3 \cdot 05 \times 10$ cm.

Area, l^2
  1 cm.^{2} = $1 \cdot 08 \times 10^{-3}$ ft.^{2} 1 ft.^{2} = $9 \cdot 29 \times 10^2$ cm.^{2}

Volume, l^3
  1 cm.^{3} = $3 \cdot 53 \times 10^{-5}$ ft.^{3} 1 ft.^{3} = $2 \cdot 83 \times 10^4$ cm.^{3}

Mass, m
  1 gm. = $2 \cdot 20 \times 10^{-3}$ lb.   1 lb. = $4 \cdot 54 \times 10^2$ gm.

Density, $\rho = m/l^3$
  1 gm./cm.^{3} = $6 \cdot 24 \times 10$ lb./ft.^{3} 1 lb./ft.^{3} = $1 \cdot 60 \times 10^{-2}$ gm./cm.^{3}
  1 kg./m.^{3} = $6 \cdot 24 \times 10^{-2}$ lb./ft.^{3} 1 lb./ft.^{3} = $1 \cdot 60 \times 10$ kg./m.^{3}

Pressure, $p = m/l\tau^2$
  1 gm. weight/cm.^{2} = 10 kg. weight/m.^{2} = $2 \cdot 05$ lb. weight/ft.^{2}
                              = $1 \cdot 42 \times 10^{-2}$ lb. weight/in.^{2}
  1 dyne/cm.^{2} = $2 \cdot 09 \times 10^{-3}$ lb. weight/ft.^{2} = $1 \cdot 45 \times 10^{-5}$ lb. weight/in.^{2}
              = $6 \cdot 72 \times 10^{-2}$ poundal/ft.^{2} = $4 \cdot 67 \times 10^{-4}$ poundal/in.^{2}
  1 lb. weight/in.^{2} = $6 \cdot 89 \times 10^4$ dyne/cm.^{2} = $4 \cdot 63 \times 10^3$ poundal/ft.^{2}
                              = $3 \cdot 22 \times 10$ poundal/in.^{2}

Force, $F = ml/\tau^2$
  1 gm. weight = $9 \cdot 81 \times 10^2$ dyne = $2 \cdot 20 \times 10^{-3}$ lb. weight
                          = $7 \cdot 09 \times 10^{-2}$ poundal.
  1 lb. weight = $4 \cdot 54 \times 10^2$ gm. weight = $4 \cdot 45 \times 10^5$ dyne
                          = $3 \cdot 22 \times 10$ poundal.
  1 poundal = $3 \cdot 11 \times 10^{-2}$ lb. weight = $1 \cdot 41 \times 10$ gm. weight
                          = $1 \cdot 38 \times 10^4$ dyne.

Temperature, t or T
  $t°$ C. = $(1 \cdot 8t + 32)°$ F. $t°$ F. = $\left(\dfrac{t-32}{1 \cdot 8}\right)$ °C.
  $t°$ C. = $T°$ C. Abs. = $(t + 273)°$ C. Abs.
  $t°$ F. = $T°$ F. Abs. = $(t + 460)°$ F. Abs.

Heat, Q
  1 cal. = $3 \cdot 97 \times 10^{-3}$ B.Th.U.   1 B.Th.U. = $2 \cdot 52 \times 10^2$ cal.
  1 kilocal. = $3 \cdot 97$ B.Th.U.   1 B.Th.U. = $2 \cdot 52 \times 10^{-1}$ kilocal.

Heat transfer per unit time, $b = Q/\tau$
  1 cal./sec. = $3 \cdot 60$ kilocal./hr. = $1 \cdot 43 \times 10$ B.Th.U./hr.
                          = $4 \cdot 19 \times 10^{-3}$ kilowatt.
  1 kilowatt = $3 \cdot 41 \times 10^3$ B.Th.U./hr. = $8 \cdot 59 \times 10^2$ kilocal./hr.
                          = $2 \cdot 39 \times 10^2$ cal./sec.

Heat transfer per unit time per unit area, $H = b/l^2 = Q/\tau l^2$
  1 cal./cm.^{2} sec. = $1 \cdot 33 \times 10^4$ B.Th.U./ft.^{2} hr.
  1 kilocal./m.^{2} hr. = $3 \cdot 69 \times 10^{-1}$ B.Th.U./ft.^{2} hr.

1 B.Th.U./ft.^{2} hr. $= 7.53 \times 10^{-5}$ cal./cm.^{2} sec.

$\qquad = 2.71$ kilocal./m.^{2} hr.

Heat transfer per unit time per unit area per unit temperature difference,
'*Heat transfer coefficient*', $\alpha = H/\theta = b/l^2\theta = Q/\tau l^2\theta$

1 cal./cm.^{2} sec. °C. $= 7.37 \times 10^3$ B.Th.U./ft.^{2} hr. °F.

1 kilocal./m.^{2} hr. °C. $= 2.05 \times 10^{-1}$ B.Th.U./ft.^{2} hr. °F.

1 B.Th.U./ft.^{2} hr. °F. $= 1.36 \times 10^{-4}$ cal./cm.^{2} sec. °C.

1 B.Th.U./ft.^{2} hr. °F. $= 4.88$ kilocal./m.^{2} hr. °C.

Specific heat per unit mass, $c = Q/mt$

1 cal./gm. °C. $= 1$ kilocal./kg. °C. $= 1$ B.Th.U./lb. °F.

Specific heat per unit volume, $s = Q/l^3t$

1 cal./cm.^{3} °C. $= 10^3$ kilocal./m.^{3} °C. $= 6.24 \times 10$ B.Th.U./ft.^{3} °F.

1 B.Th.U./ft.^{3} °F. $= 1.60 \times 10^{-2}$ cal./cm.^{3} °C.

$\qquad = 1.60 \times 10$ kilocal./m.^{3} °C.

Thermal conductivity, $k = Q/l\tau t$

1 cal./cm. sec. °C. $= 2.42 \times 10^2$ B.Th.U./ft. hr. °F.

1 kilocal./m. hr. °C. $= 6.72 \times 10^{-1}$ B.Th.U./ft. hr. °F.

1 B.Th.U./ft. hr. °F. $= 4.13 \times 10^{-3}$ cal./cm. sec. °C.

1 B.Th.U./ft. hr. °F. $= 1.49$ kilocal./m. hr. °C.

Viscosity, $\mu = m/l\tau$

1 gm./cm. sec. $= 1$ poise $= 2.42 \times 10^2$ lb./ft. hr.

1 lb./ft. hr. $= 4.13 \times 10^{-3}$ gm./cm. sec.

Kinematic viscosity or thermal diffusivity, $\nu = l^2/\tau$

1 cm.^{2}/sec. $= 3.87$ ft.^{2}/hr. $\qquad$ 1 ft.^{2}/hr. $= 2.58 \times 10^{-1}$ cm.^{2}/sec.

Miscellaneous

1 ft.^{3} of water weighs 62.4 lb. $\qquad$ 1 gallon water weighs 10 lb.

1 in. water $= 5.20$ lb./ft.$^2 = 3.61 \times 10^{-2}$ lb./in.^{2}

Acceleration due to gravity, $g = 3.22 \times 10$ ft./sec.^{2}

$\qquad\qquad\qquad\qquad\qquad = 4.17 \times 10^8$ ft./hr.^{2}

$\log_e x = 2.30 \log_{10} x$.

Latent heat of steam, q, at 212° F. $= 539$ cal./gm. $= 970$ B.Th.U./lb.

INDEX OF NAMES

INDEX OF SUBJECTS

PRINTED IN
GREAT BRITAIN
AT THE
UNIVERSITY PRESS
OXFORD
BY
CHARLES BATEY
PRINTER
TO THE
UNIVERSITY